D1294237

The Old Familiar
Booby Traps of Home

The Old Familiar Booby Traps of Home

WILL STANTON

1977

DOUBLEDAY & COMPANY, INC.
GARDEN CITY, NEW YORK

Library of Congress Cataloging in Publication Data:
ISBN: 0-385-12552-6
Library of Congress Catalog Card Number: 76-42399
COPYRIGHT © 1962, 1963, 1966, 1975, 1976, 1977 BY WILL STANTON
ALL RIGHTS RESERVED
PRINTED IN THE UNITED STATES OF AMERICA
FIRST EDITION

Grateful acknowledgment is made for permission to include excerpts from the
following copyrighted publications:

Portions of "Try a Little Tenderness," Copyright 1932 by Campbell Connelly,
Inc., renewed © 1960 by Robbins Music Corporation. Used by permission of
Robbins Music Corporation.

"Promissory Note" and "Hold the Phone" appeared in *Look* as "Keep Off
These Promises" and "All-Tolled;" "Imperfect Listener," "You Know How It
Is with Women," "Hold the Phone," *Ladies' Home Journal*; "Hello, Dali,"
The Reader's Digest, Copyright © 1967 The Reader's Digest Association, Inc.;
"Goblins, Go Home" and "Happy New Year, Mrs. Robinson," *The Reader's
Digest*, the latter as "This Year It's Going to Be Different," Copyright ©
1968 The Reader's Digest Association, Inc.; "Did Somebody Call Me Cupid?"
"The Chick Chick Syndrome," "The Old Familiar Booby Traps of Home,"
The Reader's Digest, as "Just Call Me Cupid," "Operation Easter Bunny,"
"Home Is Where the Harm Is," Copyright © 1971, 1972, 1973 The Reader's
Digest Association, Inc., respectively; "Power Play" and "Homework," *The
Reader's Digest* as "Never Underestimate the Power" and "Home Sweet Home-
work!" Copyright © 1974 The Reader's Digest Association, Inc.; "The 32nd of
March" and "Down the White Water," *The Reader's Digest* as "No Fool
Like an April Fool" and "Just Call Me Pathfinder," Copyright © 1975 The
Reader's Digest Association, Inc.; "Courtin' Time" and "Only a Game," *The
Reader's Digest*, the latter as "Get All These Wonderful Contestants?" Copy-
right © 1976 The Reader's Digest Association, Inc.; "Never Forget Jofs and
Toks," *McCall's* as "Everything You Need to Know About Married Life,"
Copyright © 1975 The McCall Publishing Company; "Huckleberry Finn—Get
Lost," *McCall's* as "Thanks for the Memories," Copyright © 1976 The McCall
Publishing Company; "Return to Marvin Gardens," "Gift Horse" as "Mother's
Day, Etc." "Farewell, St. Nick" and "The Losing Game," *Woman's Day
Magazine*, reprinted by permission of *Woman's Day Magazine*, a Fawcett pub-
lication.

Contents

Introduction

I have been asked to write something to clarify the ages and relationships of the people in this book. Nothing could be simpler. When I wrote the first story, which actually doesn't happen to be the first chapter, my wife and I had boys of nine and seven and a girl, six. I gave them the names Maggie, Roy, Sammy, and Gretchen. We also had some younger boys, but they don't enter the picture at this point. Okay?

I used these people in several stories and all went well. Then I noticed that Roy was getting a little old for the part he was supposed to be playing so I had the kid playing Sammy take over Roy's part and one of the little kids took over Sammy's part. This meant Gretchen was now older than Sammy, but I didn't think anybody would care. Fair enough?

The years go by, more stories appear and it's time for a new kid to take over Sammy's role. Sammy moves up to Roy's part. Roy is phased out. Gretchen is now older than both Sammy and Roy, so she becomes Kit. If there happens to be a part for a pre-school kid we move back to the time when Sammy was four. We don't have any more girls coming along, so when there is a part for a younger girl, Kit becomes Gretchen again, occasionally she is both. All right?

Maggie says why keep phasing them out? When the kids get to be twelve or fourteen why not write about kids who are twelve or fourteen? Mainly I guess I don't want to. When you are seven or eight, it seems like twelve- and fourteen-year-olds are the greatest people in the world. When you're fourteen you admire twenty-year-olds the most. But when you're forty-five or fifty, it seems as though seven- and eight-year-olds are the best. "I've got to phase them out," I tell Maggie. "In fact I may just phase everybody out." She says if it comes to phasing out the narrator would I mind phasing in somebody more like George Segal? Whoever he is.

So there you have it. As clarified as anything that goes on around this place. And a lot clearer than most. Okay?

The Old Familiar
Booby Traps of Home

Happy New Year, Mrs. Robinson

New Year's resolutions are like anything else—you get out of them what you put into them. Judging from results other years, I had never put enough in, but this year was different. I had been reading a book on self-improvement entitled *The Golden Web* or *The Golden Beam* or something like that. I've noticed that women who write these spirited-type books usually have gold in the title somewhere.

Anyhow, that's where I got my resolutions: (Find some beauty in everything.) (Make the other fellow feel important.) About thirty of them. According to the book anyone who followed all these rules would be blessed with a richer life, boundless love from his family, and the admiration and affection of the entire community—maybe even the whole state. I could hardly wait until New Year's to try it out.

When I came downstairs, Maggie was at the kitchen sink. I tiptoed over and gave her a kiss on the back of the neck. Resolution No. 1. (Try to be more spontaneous in showing affection.) She gave a little cry and dropped a cup. "My God, don't ever sneak up on me like that," she said. (If you're going to be spontaneous, better scuff a little.)

"You're looking lovely this morning," I said. (A sincere compliment is worth its weight in gold.)

"Look," she said, "it wasn't my idea to stay out until 4:00 A.M. and all the people coming for open house this evening."

I got some aspirin and coffee and took them in the living room. I'd just started the paper when Sammy came in. He was wearing the watch he'd gotten for Christmas. "Dad," he said, "what makes a watch run?"

In the old days I probably would have told him to ask his mother. Instead I said I'd show him. (Always encourage your child's curiosity.) I got a pencil and started a simple sketch of the escapement mechanism. It took about fifteen minutes and Sammy started to wander off several times, but I called him back. "There," I said, "that's what makes your watch run."

"Then how come it doesn't?" he asked.

Roy happened to be walking by. "You have to wind it," he said. Sammy wound it and held it to his ear. He smiled.

"Roy sure is smart," he said.

I smiled, but I didn't say anything. (Count to ten and think again.) I find it works if you use Roman numerals. I picked up my paper, and Gretchen came in with her doll, Mrs. Robinson.

"Morning, Gretchen," I said, "Happy New Year." She looked at me and then at the doll. "Happy New Year, Mrs. Robinson," I added. (Meet your child at his own level.)

"This isn't Mrs. Robinson," she said, "it's Bonnie Parker. Mrs. Robinson is sick."

"I'm sorry to hear it," I said. "What seems to be the matter?"

She shrugged. "Probably a coronary."

"Why don't you take her to see Dr. Sammy?" I suggested. "He can use his new doctor's kit. Excuse me." I went into the hall to answer the phone.

It was a friend of Kit's. "Happy New Year, Marilyn," I said. "What have you been doing over the holidays?" (Show an interest in your children's friends.) She said nothing much. "A pretty girl like you," I said jovially, "I'll bet the fellows are swarming around your house. What's that?" I asked. "Yes, of course you can speak to Kit. Certainly."

Kit was in her room with the record player going. I rapped on the door. She called out something and I went in. She was still in pajamas. "I didn't say you could come in," she yelled, grabbing up a robe and holding it in front of her. At fourteen she has become overaware of being female.

"I'm sorry, I couldn't understand you." To ease the situation, I picked up her brand-new sweater from the floor and put it over a chair.

"I was going to pick it up," she said defensively. "You don't always put your things away."

I smiled. "That's very true." There was a series of shrieks from across the hall.

I found Gretchen in tears. Roy and Sammy were about to perform open-heart surgery on Mrs. Robinson with a scout knife. "She told us she was sick," Roy said.

"I'm sure she had something else in mind," I said. "Give her a pill and use your knife for something else." They wanted to know what else. I suggested they carve something for their mother—like a salad spoon. That should keep them occupied for a while. (Encourage creativity in the young.)

Downstairs Maggie wanted to know what was wrong with Gretchen.

"Mrs. Robinson had a coronary," I told her.

"Look," she said, "I know you're not feeling your best after last night, and I've tried to make allowances, but I'm getting a little tired of these smart remarks. Would you mind taking the garbage out?"

"Not a bit," I said. (The most trivial chore can prove rewarding if approached with zest.) "I'd be happy to."

"That's what I mean," she said.

It seemed to me my resolutions weren't working the way the book had said. I didn't quit, though. I helped the boys build a snowman, only Sammy got his feet wet and Roy lost his mittens and they went inside. I played jacks with Gretchen, but she said I didn't do it right. I struck up a conversation with Kit, trying to establish some kind of rapport. I touched on hippies, pop music, dating, morality, etc. However, she contributed very little. Just about anybody else would have thrown in the sponge, but I kept trying. For example, taking down the tree is a job Maggie always dreads, so I thought I'd do it and surprise her. (Take over one of your wife's chores and she'll love you for it.)

I was about two-thirds done when Maggie came in. She stopped dead still. "What in the name of heaven are you doing?"

"Coloring Easter eggs," I said. (A touch of humor is never amiss.)

"Oh no," she said. "I wanted it left up for the party tonight."

"O.K." I said cheerfully. "I'll redecorate it. No problem there," and I reached over and gave her a playful slap. Apparently she wasn't in a playful mood. She jumped.

"Oh, Lord," she said, "can't you just sit down and watch a football game? Please?" I knew she meant well, but I had better things to do. I got all the stuff out of the boxes and started putting them back on the tree. I was doing fine when the phone rang. It was Maggie's mother. She said she was sorry to take me away from my football game.

"I wasn't watching," I said, "I was decorating the tree." She didn't say anything. "The Christmas tree," I added. "We got a beauty this year."

"I know," she said. "I saw it at Christmas. If it's the same one."

"Oh, sure," I said. "Same old tree. Same old decorations. You know us." I gave a lighthearted laugh. "Just a second and I'll call Maggie."

I couldn't help hearing part of the conversation. "About four o'clock," Maggie said. "Well, certainly he's been to bed." There was a pause and the hall door closed. I went back to work on the tree.

After a while Maggie came in. "It looks fine," she said. "Why don't you let me finish up and you go watch your game?"

14

I said, "I can't understand why you and your mother are so damned eager for me to watch football."

"It's what you usually do on New Year's."

"This year is different."

"Yes," she said, "isn't it?" She went over to the couch and sat down. "I swear I don't know," she said. "The kids have been impossible all day. I found the boys whittling on my best salad spoon and then they had the nerve to say you suggested it. One of Gretchen's jacks got in the vacuum and she said you'd left it there. And Kit has been in a poisonous mood. She said Marilyn called and you didn't tell her. She said you were snooping around her room making sarcastic—"

"Snooping, my eye!" I said. "If a man can't take a fatherly interest—"

"She said you cross-examined Marilyn about her boy friends."

"Oh, my God!" I said. "Marilyn's boy friends are the least of my concerns by an overwhelming margin. I was only making a little small talk." The kids were filtering into the room, drawn by the commotion.

"You never bothered with small talk before, why start now?"

"Because it's New Year's," I said. "That and the jacks and the tree were all part of my resolutions."

She stared at me. "I don't believe you," she said flatly.

"It's true." I explained to them about the book and what I'd been trying to accomplish. There was a moment of silence. The kids were standing there looking at each other uneasily. "A man wants to improve himself," I said. "Be a better husband, a better father—"

Maggie said, "Didn't you think we liked you the way you were?"

"Well," I said, "sure, I suppose so."

"We all want to be better," she said. "Only when you're so cheerful and considerate about everything it doesn't seem natural. If the kids do something and you get mad, they know where they stand. But when you're always so even-tempered—"

"Yeah," Kit said. "You didn't say anything about my record

player or the clothes on the floor. You just smiled. It gave me the creeps."

Roy said, "I been in more trouble today than any New Year's I remember."

Gretchen said, "I think it was better when you didn't play jacks."

"And yelled," Sammy said, "and said damnitall."

"All right," I said, "that's enough! I make every effort to be a good father and all the thanks I get you could stick in your eye. The fact is you kids don't deserve a good father. You don't even deserve the father you've got." I was moving about, illustrating my points with appropriate gestures. "You're the ones that better start making resolutions. Like doing your homework, cleaning your rooms, letting the spoons alone. And when I tell you to do something you damned well better jump." I reached out to steady a lamp I had brushed with my sleeve. "Furthermore—" I realized suddenly the atmosphere had changed. The kids were sprawled on the floor, relaxed, whispering—I turned to Maggie. "What the hell is everybody smiling about?" I asked. "What's the big joke?"

"No joke," she said. "We're just happy to have you back again."

Return to Marvin Gardens

The other day I asked Maggie if she thought our children were equipped to meet the challenges of today's world. She looked down at me from the ladder. She was painting the gutters on the garage at the time.

"Do I think what?" she asked. I repeated the question. "What have they done now?" she wanted to know.

"They've started a game of Monopoly," I said, "and I'm not at all happy with the way they're playing it." She didn't answer. I looked up. "Do you always paint with your eyes closed?" I asked.

She said she was just thinking.

"Sammy buys any junk property he can lay his hands on," I said, "Gretchen only wants the lots with pretty names. Roy hates to part with any cash."

"It's only a game," she said.

"Very true," I said. "And life is a game if you want to look at it that way."

"Why not?" she said. She reached out for a spot she'd missed and I felt a splatter of paint drops across my face. "Sorry," she said.

"Maggie," I said, "why don't you ever wipe the extra paint off your brush?"

"Because I thought you'd have more sense than to stand right underneath," she said.

I walked away. It seemed to me a man should be able to have a discussion with his wife without putting on a drop cloth. When I went back she had moved to the other side of the garage. "Maggie," I said, "would you believe that you can learn a lot about a person by watching him play Monopoly?"

"Sure thing," she said. "If he keeps yelling at the other players, punches them a lot—"

"I'm not joking," I said. "A fellow that's reckless and foolhardy at Monopoly is going to be the same way on the job, in the home, on the highway—"

"And o'er the deep blue sea," Maggie said.

"You know, I've always been quite a student of the game. Maybe you remember when we were engaged we used to play all the time."

"Did we really? I thought it just seemed like all the time."

"Watching Sammy play I got to thinking of your mother's cousin Wallace, the one that used to go to all the tax sales. He owned little pie-shaped pieces of property all over the county. Half the time he didn't even know where they were. And when he did locate one there'd usually be four or five junked cars on it."

"Pie-shaped actually means round," Maggie said, "if you want to be technical. What *you* mean is wedge-shaped." She reached out to scrape off some loose paint with the heel of her brush. Little Miss Technical.

"Your Uncle Otis was like Roy," I said, "liked to keep all his savings in hard cash. I remember when your Aunt Binnie got her inheritance and invested in that company that made artificial frogs to put on the lawn. Otis never got over it. Used to tell everybody that real greenbacks weren't good enough for Binnie, she had to invest in fake ones. And year in and year out the artificial greenbacks went up and the real ones went down."

Maggie had gotten off the ladder and was tugging it along between the garage and the rosebush. One of the vines had caught her across the firm part of the slacks and another had her by the blouse so she couldn't move her arms. "I seem to have a problem," she said.

"I know," I said, "you've had it a long time. As I've so often remarked—"

"Will you kindly get me out of here?"

"Just let me say one thing," I said. "From the first game I noticed you had a tendency to rush into things—sell the Water Works, buy the B & O. But you never worked from a plan, never considered what might lie ahead, or behind as the case might be."

She tried to move the ladder back out, the can tottering and the paint slopping over. "If you'll just be patient," I said, "I'll get some gloves and have you out in a jiffy." When I got back the rosebush had been trampled flat, there was paint splattered all about and Maggie was up on the ladder again. I chuckled. "Looks like the old B & O is back on the tracks." She didn't say anything. Not until the next day.

I decided the best way to teach the kids was to pretend I'd forgotten the game and let them teach me. Roy was banker and he counted out five thousand dollars each. I said it used to be fifteen hundred dollars. Inflation Gretchen said. "What inflation?" I asked, "the lots are the same price as ever." Roy said after I'd played for a while I'd catch on.

"You can't expect to get it all at once," Sammy said.

Gretchen was first and got Oriental Avenue for a hundred dollars. Sammy landed on Vermont in the same block. He tried to make a deal with Gretchen but she wouldn't sell. She wouldn't buy either. "Keep your stinking lot," she told him.

I landed on INCOME TAX—PAY $200. Roy lit on Connecticut. I pointed out that each of them owned a third of the block. "One of you ought to buy out the other two and start putting up houses." Nobody wanted to. Okay, I thought, learn it the hard way.

Gretchen landed on St. Charles Place. Sammy got the Pennsylvania Railroad. Roy got the Electric Company. I got VISITING JAIL. My next roll put me on Community Chest. I took the top card from the pile. YOU BACKED INTO A HOUSE PAY EVERYBODY $50. "Now just a minute," I said, "this isn't a regular card—it's written in pencil."

Some of the cards had gotten lost, Roy said, so they had made up some new ones. I didn't think it was very fair, but I paid. When I finally got to GO, I collected my two hundred dollars, but it had cost me over three hundred dollars to get there. Half the property was gone and I still didn't own anything.

"You sure have got bad luck," Sammy said.

I explained that there was no such thing as bad luck. "A slow start is one thing, but bad luck is only an excuse that poor players use." I rolled and landed on Connecticut. Roy said that would be eight dollars.

"You see?" I said, "if you'd done what I told you and bought the other two lots the rent would have been double."

He put the eight dollars on his stack. "You sure do learn fast." My next roll landed me on New York Avenue. Also Roy's. That one was twenty dollars.

"Man," Sammy said, "when you start slow you stay slow."

"When I want advice I'll ask for it," I told him. "Roll the dice."

Gretchen had to go to the bathroom. I went to the kitchen and poured myself a drink. Maggie asked how it was going.

"Such bad luck you wouldn't believe," I said.

"I thought you didn't believe in luck."

"I don't, but when a top-notch player loses to a bunch of kids, how else do you explain it?" She said she didn't know.

"They haven't the foggiest notion of the game," I said. "Sammy had two lots I wanted and he sold me one for a hundred and eighty dollars—that's a hundred less than he paid for it."

"What about the other one?"

"He wanted eighteen hundred for that one. Can you beat it?" She mumbled something about bait and switch, but she was eating a pretzel and I couldn't quite make it out.

"Naturally I wouldn't pay any such ridiculous amount, and while I was trying to talk some sense into him both Roy and Gretchen landed on the lot. I could see the longer I waited the more rent I'd lose so I finally told him I'd meet his price."

"You mean you actually paid the eighteen hundred dollars?"

"Actually no. By then it had gone up to twenty-one hundred. He said it was his best money-maker."

Maggie choked on a piece of pretzel. I pounded her on the back. "You'll come out on top," she said. "They're not in your league."

She was right of course. Only a weak player lets a losing streak influence his play. I went back and put another house on each of my lots. The next round I ran out of cash and had to sell back the houses at half price.

Back in the kitchen Maggie asked if my luck had changed.

It wasn't just luck I told her. "The boys are in cahoots. If one goes broke the other bails him out."

"Isn't that against the rules—lending money?"

"They don't actually lend it. They sell each other Baltic Avenue for a thousand dollars."

"They sound like a couple of real little sharpies."

"Gretchen's just as bad," I said. "Remember Free Parking? Gretchen bought it. Costs eighty dollars now."

"That reminds me," she said, "I need some change for the paper boy."

"Don't look at me," I told her, "I'm cleaned out."

She stared. "You're not playing for real money?"

I laughed. "No, Sammy is starting a rare-coin store. I happened to have a couple of rare old quarters in my pocket—in fact I sold him all my change—eight hundred dollars' worth."

"You mean—"

"Relax." I chuckled. "In real money it was only two—at the most three dollars."

"Wait here." She went out and came back in a moment and put something on the table. Money. Five thousand dollars in big bills. "It's from that old set we used to have."

"Maggie," I said, "what are you asking me to do?"

"Take it," she said. "Take it and win." I told her it was out of the question. "Go on," she said. "How can you teach the kids the fundamentals of the game if they have all the money?"

I fanned out the bills. It was tempting. And in a sense it was only fair. The way they played they didn't deserve to win. With a fresh stake I could take advantage of their weaknesses—show them how sound practice always pays. I could—

"No," I shoved the money away. "How can I teach them sound practice when I take money from under the table?"

"I'm glad," she said simply. "I was hoping you wouldn't take it, but it had to be your decision."

I patted her on the shoulder. "Don't sell the old pro short." I went back to the game.

Roy was looking out the window. "Hey," he said, "they're starting a ball game across the street. Let's go."

"Sit down," I told him. "Sit down and roll the dice." I looked around the table. "School is now in session."

Maggie was still in the kitchen. She asked me how it was going. I didn't answer. I sat down in the breakfast nook, staring across at the other bench, my hands resting on the table.

"What is it?" She slid into the seat across from me. "What's wrong?"

"Listen—" my voice was husky, I had to keep clearing my throat. "Have you still got the five grand?"

"The money? Of course." She went over and got it from the shelf.

"I know how you feel about this—" I said.

"Don't be ridiculous." She opened my fist, put the money inside and closed my fingers around it. "It's yours. You deserve it."

"It's only for a little while—till I get back on my feet."

"Your luck still bad?"

"Even when it's not my turn. Gretchen got a Chance card— SCHOOL TAX—YOUR FATHER HAS TO PAY $225."

Maggie was indignant. "That just isn't fair."

I shrugged. "Neither is life if it comes to that. Then there's insurance. I have to pay Sammy a hundred and ninety dollars every time I pass Mediterranean Avenue."

"What do you mean, you have to pay Sammy?"

"Actually I pay it to the Godfather Protection Agency. It belongs to whoever owns Mediterranean. And there was three hundred and fifty dollars to Roy. He owns the Electric Company."

"You couldn't possibly—"

"It wasn't for the bill," I explained, "it was the charge for turning on the air conditioner. Well," I said, "it was like an oven in there."

"If you ask me," she said, "it's all one big racket."

"You haven't heard the worst," I said. "Gretchen owns the Water Works."

It was about half an hour later when I came back to the kitchen. "We got any toothpicks?" I asked Maggie. "I've got a piece of popcorn between my teeth." She wanted to know where I'd gotten popcorn. I said I bought it from Roy. "He makes it in that electric popper he got."

"What do you mean you bought it?"

"He sells it," I said. "Two-fifty a bowl." She said she didn't believe it. "It's true. He's got a popcorn stand on St. James Place. Sammy has the pretzel concession on all the railroads. Gretchen sells homemade fudge."

"You don't mean you actually encourage them?"

"At seventy-five dollars for one pretzel? What do you take me for?"

"Don't ask me," she said. "You're the one with the popcorn in your teeth."

"Yes. You see Sammy bought a bowl from Roy. Money isn't everything, he said. Roy bought two pretzels from Sammy. He liked to encourage the small-business man, he said. Well, I've said the same things many times. And I didn't want to look cheap—especially after Roy offered me one of the pretzels."

"Nobody likes to look cheap."

"What really bothers me is Gretchen. Asking three hundred and fifty dollars for a piece of fudge. She's going to ruin a good thing."

"Still, it's only play money."

23

"I'm perfectly aware of that," I said. "But even so—three hundred and fifty dollars—and such little tiny pieces."

I never got a chance to make my comeback, but there's always another day. Of course the game has changed since I learned it. You can't just sit back on your property any more, you have to diversify—pretzels, air conditioners, whatever. And I'll give our three credit—any kid who learns to moonlight before he's out of grammar school is made of the right stuff.

But don't count me out yet. The next time we play I'm going to have a little surprise for them—a lemonade stand between the popcorn and the pretzels. As I told Maggie, when it comes to good old American know-how, the old dog can still teach them a few tricks. After all, Monopoly is as American as apple pie and processed cheese food. If you can make it on Baltic Avenue, you can make it on Madison Avenue. I thought Maggie might think my lemonade stand a little sneaky, but she's right there with me. Make them pay an extra fifty dollars for sugar she says.

That's one more thing we can learn from Monopoly—it always helps to have a good woman by your side.

Hello, Dali

Fellow was telling me about a new art form called a happening. What you do is get a hall and play music and show a movie at the same time. Also get some people to dance and somebody to read poetry. Get somebody else to splash paint on the wall and on the dancers and the poet. Scatter some seaweed around if you have any. That's about it. Art is everywhere. We don't always recognize it, is the trouble.

Decided to make some wine a while back. Squeezed the grapes and put the juice in a jug with sugar and yeast. Too much yeast maybe. Put the jug on top of the freezer out of the way. That was Friday. Next morning Maggie woke me up. Said I'd better do something. Got dressed and went out to the kitchen.

Stuff had started to work during the night. Purple foam was coming out of the jug, down the freezer, across the floor. Place smelled like abandoned fruit stand. Gnats from all over, lurching and reeling. Took jug into bathroom and put it in the tub.

Had breakfast and went into the living room. Read the paper. Daddy Warbucks got it again. Blam! Kit was wearing a hair dryer and practicing the guitar. Not easy. Maggie had to do some shopping. Told me to look after the kids. Said I would. Roy and Sammy were watching TV. Terrible picture. Fellow was supposed to come and fix it.

Went over to the window and looked out. Sammy asked what I was looking at. Told him nothing. Asked me if I'd seen a squirrel. Told him no. Asked me if I'd almost seen a squirrel. Said yes. Anything to shut him up. Didn't work. Asked me how many people I knew. Told him forty-two. Asked me who they were. Told him Fred. Who else? Ursala. Who else? Said that was all I could remember.

Roy wanted to know if he could use a rolling pin. Asked him what for. Said he wanted to roll out modeling clay. Told him to use a bottle. Out of the trash.

Kit went to her room. Told her to put the dryer away. Didn't hear me. Went into the bathroom to see how the wine was doing. Cat in the tub playing with the foam. Tried to catch it but couldn't. Cat went through living room. Left purple paw prints on the rug. All the way across. More blue than purple actually.

Fellow came about the TV. Poked around. Didn't help it any. Said probably antenna was out of adjustment. A lot of it going around. Asked me to watch picture and tell him when it looked better. Said he'd holler when ready. Told him to call down through the chimney. Noticed the fireplace needed cleaning out. Got the wheelbarrow to put ashes in. Changed my mind and decided to do something about the rug.

Got pail of water and started to wash out prints. No dice. Used more water. Finally the whole bucket. Sammy kicked it over. Soaked whole side of the rug. Wasn't going to do the floor any good either. Lifted up edge of rug and shoved wheelbarrow under it to keep it off the floor and let it dry. Put the hair dryer on top of it and turned it on. Couldn't do any harm.

Roy said there was a lady at the door. Turned out to be old school chum of Maggie's. Harriet something or other.

"I've been wanting to meet you and your wonderful family for ages," she said.

Told her Maggie ought to be back soon. Went into the living room. Harriet got part way and stopped. Said, "Oh."

"Cat ran across the rug," I explained. Tracks were right there in front of her, across the rug and up to the wet part over the wheelbarrow. Self-explanatory.

Roy had left the bottle on the floor. Put it in waste basket. Gin bottle. Told Harriet to sit down.

"I can just as well come back later," she said. "I don't want to disturb you." Told her I hadn't been doing anything. Turned off sound on TV. Left picture on. Harriet sat on edge of chair. Knees together. Hands clasped.

Sammy said, "My dad almost saw a squirrel."

Harriet jumped. Said, "That's nice, dear." Not much of a conversationalist.

Kit came in with the guitar. Introduced her to Harriet. "When are you going to take the wine out of the bathtub?" she asked. Told her there was no rush. "I want to take a bath," she said. Told her should have thought of that when she washed her hair. Save water. Waste not want not. Harriet waved her hand, brushing off gnats.

Sammy said, "My dad knows forty-two people." Harriet smiled. Lots of teeth.

Sammy said, "He can only remember the names of two of them."

Harriet said, "Oh?" Limited vocabulary. Fixed smile. Still fighting the gnats.

Sun came out. Mentioned it to Harriet. Small talk. Put her at ease.

"Yes," she said, "it looked like rain earlier, but I think it's clearing up."

TV picture faded and came back sharp and bright.

"Excuse me." Went over and yelled up chimney. "That's fine. Hold it right there."

Voice answered. Hollow-sounding. "I thought that would clear it up. Be right down." Turned around. Harriet gone. Flighty sort of woman.

Maggie came back and saw the rug. Looked thoughtful. Mentioned Harriet to her. Kids all got in two cents' worth. Took about an hour.

Maggie leaned back on couch. Eyes closed. "Harriet was one of my best friends," she said. "What will she tell people?"

Very little was my guess.

"I was only gone a short time," she said. "How could all this have happened?"

Suddenly all was clear. A happening. A work of art had taken place right in our house. Explained to Maggie.

Maggie said, "Don't speak to me."

Asked her if it didn't mean anything that her own children had participated in an aesthetic event.

No answer. Hasn't spoken to me yet. No buttons on shirts. Holes in socks. Cold toast. No matter.

Beauty is everywhere. Art will endure.

The Losing Game

When you decide to go on a diet, the first thing is to read all the books you can find and pick out the one that suits you best.

This is not as easy as it sounds, because people who write diet books are very possessive about fat people. They hate to see even one get away. They are tough-minded and glib as used-car salesmen. They can give you a dozen reasons why you should deal with them and not the fellow across the street. He won't give you a true weight loss. His diet is all talk and in ninety days you'll weigh more than ever.

The number one problem with dieting in this country is lack of leadership. It seems like all our first-rate minds are occupied with something else.

For example, one writer was showing how snacks can add up. If you ate just four potato chips, she said, working off the extra calories would require half an hour of ironing or twelve minutes of carpentering. Now, anybody who talks about eating four potato

THE OLD FAMILIAR BOOBY TRAPS OF HOME

chips hasn't been around fat people much. As for carpenters, we had one in not long ago and the first thing he did was look to see what he had in his lunch box. After that he went to the bathroom and then phoned his bridge teacher for an appointment. So when you're talking about twelve minutes of carpentering, you're dealing with something hard to pin down.

Another of the experts included a table showing the amount of carbohydrates in various foods. One of the entries said: "Frogs' legs—raw—3½ oz.—none." My question is, do you want to place your physical well-being in the hands of people like this?

The low-carbohydrate, drinking man's diet was one that struck me as particularly civilized. Besides I already had an ace in the hole. I had never cared for the rich desserts that are the downfall of so many dieters. Cheese and brandy was plenty for me.

At dinner the first night I passed up the mashed potatoes. My son Roy wanted to know how come he had to eat them and I didn't. "Because you aren't trying to lose weight," I told him. "If you're so anxious to skip something, skip dessert."

"Thanks a lot," Maggie said. It turned out she had made some prune whip and had told Roy and Sammy they had to eat some. "I want them to learn to like something besides pie and doughnuts."

"You heard your mother," I told them. They were stunned. Outraged. Mashed potatoes and prune whip both? And I got to skip them? Wasn't I the one who was always talking about fair play? I finally had to take a helping of mashed potatoes just to shut them up.

After a week with no results, Maggie suggested I go back to carbohydrates and cut out the drinks. I was willing. The funny thing was, I hardly missed my martinis. After dinner, in place of a highball I had black coffee. And two or three pieces of cake. Brownies. Peach cobbler. My ace in the hole wasn't an ace at all. It was a queen. The one that sat in the parlor eating bread and honey.

I never found out how I did on this diet because Maggie got some new scales that showed me six pounds heavier. On the old scales if you put all your weight on your heels you could drop four pounds. On the new ones it didn't work. Nothing worked. Except if you stood on one foot at the very edge and that only lowered it about half a pound. For half a pound I couldn't be bothered. I asked Maggie what had become of the old ones. She said she'd given them away.

"What's wrong with your foot?" she asked. I told her I'd slipped off the side of the scales. "And the man at the store told me they were foolproof," she said. "That shows how much he knew."

The next evening I tried eating off a salad plate. "It's psychology," I explained to Maggie. "You take smaller portions and still have a full plate."

"You took too much," she said, "it's spilling over the edge." She placed a regular dinner plate under the salad plate. "I just washed the tablecloth." I nodded. Good-by psychology. Hello tablecloth.

Of course the boys wanted to eat off two plates. "How come Dad gets to and we don't?" Roy asked.

"He gets to do lots of things we don't," Sammy said.

"We're not supposed to talk about stuff like that at the supper table," Roy said.

"Stuff like what?" I asked.

"Never mind," Maggie said. "Finish your diet."

One clever idea for reducing is to buy clothes a size small and slim into them. Maggie was all for it. "You could use some slacks with a little style. Those you have on went out with the Whigs."

I asked the clerk to see some slacks. Something sporty in a thirty-six waist. Something for my son, he said. Something for me, I told him.

"Aha," he said, "here's just the thing."

I looked at the pants. "These are a thirty-two," I said.

"What the heck?" he said. "As long as we're only dreaming, why not go all the way?"

When I got home I put the bag on the table. "You didn't buy much." Maggie looked inside. "A necktie and three pairs of socks. These are what you're going to slim into?"

"I don't tell you how to run the house," I said, "don't tell me how to buy clothes."

One of the trials of dieting is parties—especially the ones where there are a lot of skinny people all gulping down beer and scooping up the cheese dip. Showing off. They don't impress me—*de*press is more like it, always bringing to mind the essential unfairness of life. In fact we have stopped inviting thin people to our parties.

At our last one everything was fine until Maggie served the Reubens. Flo Paxton gave a little laugh. "Oh no, Maggie," she said, "and I'm trying to lose weight."

I gave a little laugh too. "Aren't we all?" I said.

"All what?" Flo's husband asked. So I had to repeat Flo's remark just at the moment when there was one of those lulls in the conversation.

Nobody said anything, just looked at each other. It seemed to strike everybody at the same time—there wasn't a welterweight in the crowd. Just heavies. After they'd looked at each other for a minute they turned to me. What could I say? I hadn't planned a party for fat people only—all I had done was go over the list and cross off all the skinny ones. But this isn't the sort of thing you can say to a group of fat people.

I couldn't think of anything to say to them. I stood there nodding with a kind of fixed smile on my face. After a moment I took a deep breath and patted myself on the stomach.

"Come on," Flo said to her husband. They put on their coats and left. Pretty soon everybody left.

"How come?" I said to Maggie afterward, "I thought fat people were supposed to be so jolly."

"It's all in the way you approach them."

"I thought they were supposed to be a barrel of laughs."

"That's what I mean," she said.

There was one diet I had high hopes for because it seemed so logical. It allowed you to eat anything you liked so long as you balanced high- and low-calorie food. If you wanted a brownie you had to balance it with twelve stalks of celery or half a cabbage.

If everybody had been on the diet it might have worked better. We have a rule that nobody leaves the table until everybody is finished. The boys would sit there, waiting to go out and staring at me and at the half cabbage still to go. It looked as big as a millstone. And heavier. And noisier.

Again you don't notice it when everybody is chomping celery, but when you're the only one—especially at the movies.

People would turn and peer around. "What's that funny noise? Sounds like somebody eating celery. At a movie? Nobody eats celery at the movies. It sure smells like celery. You're crazy." As if there were some law that you had to eat popcorn at the movies or candy bars like a lot of sheep.

Then I started going in debt. Sometimes I simply couldn't face another bite of cabbage, so I'd put it on the tab. And it kept growing like the national debt until I finally had to face it. I could never pay back what I owed the diet. We're never going to pay off the national debt either. I don't know if anybody else realizes this. The time comes when you have to face the fact that you are never going to eat fourteen heads of raw cabbage, and accepting this failure helps you accept all failures.

One psychological trick is to associate high-calorie food with unpleasant thoughts. The book suggested that when you see a piece of pie you should picture yourself being rejected by an attractive person because of your obesity. It made sense. I decided on Sophia Loren. She's wearing one of those peasant girl outfits, just hanging around the corner in Naples. She's saying how lonely she is and I say well, I'm not doing anything. She turns those great big eyes on me and says—so?

"So," I say, "how's abouta me?" talking with an Italian accent like one of the Marx Brothers. The one with the pointy hat.

Sophia says, "You? Mama mia no! You too obesea for me!" "Okay," I say, "let'sa forget it." But she won'ta forget it. She starts to yell. "What'sa matt? You so fat likea hippo." Her voice is loud and clear, her eyes flashing. "You obesea likea blimp!" You can hear her all over Naples.

By the next time we had pie I'd forgotten all about the trick. All I knew was I felt depressed, down in the dumps. To cheer myself up, I had a second piece of pie. With vanilla ice cream.

After dinner Maggie asked what I wanted to watch. "There's a Sophia Loren movie." I said I thought she was greatly overrated.

Maggie looked surprised. "I always thought she was one of your favorites." I said in my opinion she couldn't act her way out of a paper bag.

I almost forgot exercise, which is also important psychologically. Just sitting around, you are likely to be obsessed with the thought of food. But jogging, you are more likely to be obsessed with the thought of just sitting around.

I should warn that there may be side effects. Out jogging one evening, I noticed several others running in the same direction. Was everybody in the neighborhood trying to lose weight I wondered. Then I saw a whole crowd and learned that a robbery had just taken place. I jogged on and hadn't gone two blocks before I was stopped by a patrol car. The cops seemed to think I'd been involved in the robbery.

"Look," I said, "it happened fifteen minutes ago. You think I'd only be able to get two blocks away?"

I didn't look very fast, one of them said.

"Besides," I said, "who would go to a stick up on foot? If I'd worked that heist I'd have had getaway iron with a good wheelman. I'd be long gone."

"Know a lot about it, don't you?"

"My eight-year-old boy knows that much," I said. "What's wrong with you fellows? Don't you ever watch TV?"

"Anything you say may be used against you," he said, "in a court of law."

"That's more like it," I told him.

One thing dieting does is reawaken the taste buds. Without the blue cheese, olive oil, anchovies, and the like you discover what lettuce really tastes like. Not much. Maggie tried to sell me on how great it was. "Try to imagine a chicken sandwich with no lettuce," she said. I told her to try to imagine one with just lettuce. What rabbits see in it I don't know.

Everybody on a diet has some special weakness—one thing he can't stop dreaming about. Could be corn on the cob, roast pork, creamed potatoes. With me it's baloney sandwiches. Ordinary shopping-center baloney, the kind of bread that gas stations carry and mustard out of the quart jar. When I was going to school I ate baloney sandwiches about three times a week. I didn't care if I never saw another. Yet as soon as I started my diet, that's all I could think about. Like blubber to the Eskimo or dates to the Arab, baloney sandwiches were to me.

I was lying in bed one night, dieting, and I thought I would have to have a baloney sandwich or die. I crept down to the kitchen, waking the dog who started to bark. I had to give him a slice of roast beef to shut him up, but by then Roy was standing in the doorway. He wanted to know what I was doing. Getting a drink of water, I told him. He said he'd have one too.

We sat there at the kitchen table drinking ice water. Roy said I didn't have to stay up on his account. I said I wasn't sleepy. "Me either," he said. I never knew a kid who was such a slow drinker. After he'd finally gone back to bed I looked in the refrigerator.

They say everybody has his price. And you can sympathize with someone who sells out for fame or glory. But to lie to my son and bribe my dog just for a baloney sandwich. It made me look small. I got out the roast beef, the olives, the poppy seed rolls and sweet butter, the cheesecake. If you're going to go wrong, go first class.

Half an hour later I was back in bed. Still couldn't sleep. Thinking about that baloney sandwich.

I guess the worst thing about dieting is the way food comes to dominate your life. I would catch myself looking at the clock to see how long until lunch and it was only nine forty-five.

When I was a young man the future held promises of gold with no attainment entirely out of reach. And there I was, sitting at a desk with the varnish all scratched, looking forward to cottage cheese.

What did I learn from it all? For one thing, don't change scales in the middle of a diet—unless you can find some that read less. Trading a highball for three pieces of cake is a poor bargain. If it means giving up Sophia Loren, it's even worse. Psychology is like garlic—it's not for people who keep changing their minds. And jogging toward the scene of a crime is better than jogging away from it. Other things being equal.

Did Somebody Call Me Cupid?

It burns me up the way they've commercialized Valentine's Day. As I've told Maggie, we've lost the spirit of it. "Originally a valentine was something personal," I said, "from the heart. A fellow would write some verses to his girl, something like that."

"It's certainly cheaper than flowers or candy," she said.

"That has nothing to do with it," I said. "Anybody could give those. A valentine should have a person's individual stamp.

"But today everybody thinks it's easier to pick up something at the store," I said. "And the candy people take advantage of this. They put the chocolates in a heart-shaped box and double the price. If it's candy you want," I said, "why not beat them at their own game? Wait until after Valentine's Day when they have to unload the fancy boxes at half price."

"Why not?" she said. "That idea certainly has your personal stamp on it."

Just because a person doesn't believe in throwing money away that doesn't mean he's cheap. I've never gone in for the conventional type valentine. When I was first dating Maggie I wasn't working and I wanted to give her something that was impressive but didn't cost anything. I found a boulder that was sort of heart-shaped and left it outside her back door with a humorous message on it. Unfortunately her father didn't see it when he backed out of the garage and I had to get him a new muffler. What's cheap about that?

Nobody cares about the personal touch any more. Take our boys—they were after Maggie to buy valentines to give their classmates. Sammy is in first grade and Roy's in third. "Wouldn't it be more fun to make your own?" I asked them. They said no. Maggie said that made three of them.

I was getting annoyed. "Don't you want your children to learn to do things for themselves?" I asked her, "instead of buying everything like a couple of robots?"

"Robots don't buy things," Roy said, "they make what they want."

Sammy said, "I wish you'd buy us a robot. Then he could make us valentines."

I went out and mixed a drink. Then I decided to give them one more chance. I asked the boys how they'd like to make a valentine present for their mother. They said sure. Sammy wanted to bake her a cake. Roy said he was going to make her a dress. He's always looking for an excuse to use the sewing machine. This bothers me a little. I know dress designers make a mint but even so—

I said they should think of something that didn't require power equipment. "You don't want us to buy anything," Roy said, "and now you won't let us make anything." I explained calmly and patiently that small boys can't make cakes and dresses.

"You're not supposed to swear in front of children," Roy said.

"It sets a bad example," Sammy said.

"It's past your bedtime," I told them.

The next day I bought a valentine kit and after supper we spread it out on the dining-room table. I showed them how to punch out the parts and paste on the hearts and the lace. They got paste all over the table and started fighting over the scissors. I

37

told them to cut it out. "You two are going to learn the joy of making something with your own hands," I told them, "if I have to rap your heads together." I went out for a drink.

When I got back the boys were gone. Maggie asked how it was going. I picked up a valentine to show her and the lace fell off. Cheap paste. It wouldn't stick to the paper. It stuck to everything else O.K. My glass. My cigar.

The boys still weren't back. I mixed another drink. The first one had gotten spilled. About eleven o'clock, Maggie came in. She took a sip of my drink and picked up a valentine. "Interesting," she said. "The drink tastes like paste and the valentine smells like bourbon." I said I'd noticed. "You've done eight," she said, "only fifty-seven to go."

I gave in and bought a couple of boxes of ready-made ones. They were pretty sleazy, and after the boys had put the names on I slipped a chocolate heart in each envelope for a surprise. When I got home the next day the boys wouldn't speak to me. I asked Maggie what was up. She said every kid in class had gotten a candy heart except Roy and Sammy. I hadn't thought of that.

"O.K." I said, "I'll go back and get them some." Sammy wanted to go along to leave a valentine at a girl's house. When we finally located it he wouldn't go in. He said he couldn't reach the mailbox, so I delivered it. A couple of blocks later he said, "There it is. That's Sharon's house." We'd left the valentine at the wrong place.

We went back and I got the Valentine out of the mailbox. The porch was pitch dark. As I started down the steps I met a man coming up. "You looking for me?" I said I wanted to deliver a valentine to a girl named Sharon.

"She doesn't live here," he said. I said I knew but I'd left the valentine by mistake and had to come back to get it. I showed it to him. The man sniffed. "You been drinking?" I said no, it was the valentine. I went down the steps. He followed me. "We've been bothered with prowlers around here lately," he said. He grabbed me by the sleeve.

"Look," I pointed to my car, "if I was going prowling would I take a six-year-old boy along?"

"I never met a prowler before," he said, "how the hell do I know how your mind works?"

A woman called out from the house and wanted to know what was the matter. The man called back, "Fellow here says he's got a valentine for somebody named Karen." Sharon I said. "Sharon," the man said. The woman said nobody named Sharon lived there. "Oh, for God's sake," the man said, "don't you suppose I know that? What's wrong with you?" The woman said at least she wasn't standing in the middle of the yard swearing. I went back to the car.

Sammy said, "You sure took a long time."

"If you don't like the way I deliver your valentines," I said, "you can do it yourself."

When we got back from the candy store, Maggie was waiting with Roy. She said the boys had been invited to spend the night with their friend Buster, so I drove them over. I said they might as well give the bag of chocolate hearts to Buster's mother—a little valentine present. Back home I got Maggie's present from the glove compartment and took it in.

She acted surprised. "A valentine?" She opened the bag and looked in. "Mm—chocolates." I said what did she mean chocolates? She held out the bag.

"The boys were supposed to give those to Buster's mother," I said. "My God, they must have given her your present. They were both in the glove compartment."

She said, "Maybe they didn't give her anything."

"Yes they did," I said. "She came to the door and said thanks for the valentine. I told her to enjoy it and think of me. I thought it was the candy."

Maggie looked at me. "It wasn't candy."

"No," I said, "it was a nightgown with hearts on it. A peek-a-boo nightgown." Maggie started to laugh.

"Damn it all," I said, "I was only trying to do something nice—for the boys, for Buster's mother, for you. And where did it get me?"

Maggie put her hands over her face and shook her head. She

seemed to be crying. I patted her on the shoulder. "I'm sorry," I said, "I wanted to give you a nice surprise."

"You did." She wiped her eyes. "Just the thought—" and she started to laugh again.

"I realized that trying to be original was a way of showing off," I said. "So I decided this year I was going to buy you a valentine just like other husbands. I wanted something sentimental and romantic—"

"Come here," she held out her arms. I went over to the couch. "Do I have to wear a fancy nighty to be sentimental and romantic?"

"Not for me," I said.

After a minute she said, "This is the nicest Valentine's Day I can remember." It was beginning to look better to me too. The phone started to ring.

"Probably Buster's mother," Maggie said. I said probably. It kept on ringing.

"It could be Buster's father," she said.

"Could be," I said.

"Let it ring," Maggie said.

Hold the Phone

Of all the trouble makers in history, I think the name of Alexander Graham Bell should head the list. Roughly 90 per cent of all my traumatic experiences have been somehow connected with the telephone and almost always one of the children has been involved. Like the cookie incident. It started with the PTA. Maggie was in charge of cookies for one of their functions, and since she was going to be downtown and I was going to be home I had promised to pick them up at four o'clock from some woman whose name I couldn't recall. I hung around the house figuring that eventually the woman would call to see where I was, which is what happened, and where I was when she called was at the store getting cigarettes. Kit explained it to her.

"Fine," I said when I got home, "what's her name?"

Kit thought it began with an N. That was the way I remembered it too. "Nelville?" I suggested. "Something like that?"

She shook her head. "More like Nelson."

41

That seemed to ring a bell—fortunately there was only one Nelson in the book. A man answered the phone.

I introduced myself. "I'm sorry I was out when your wife phoned," I said. He didn't say anything. "Mr. Nelson, your wife did call me, didn't she?"

"What about?" he said.

"About the cookies," I said. "I was supposed to pick them up. Your wife was going to bake six dozen—small ones."

"I see," he said. "What gave you the idea she was going to bake you these cookies?"

I could see I had got off on the wrong foot. Apparently she had neglected to tell her husband about the PTA. "She wasn't making them for me." I laughed apologetically. "As a matter of fact, I've never been much of a cookie eater."

There was a long pause. "Would you mind repeating that?" he asked.

Well, I did mind—it wasn't the sort of remark that's improved by repetition. However, Nelson was nothing to me and becoming more so by the moment. "I'm afraid I've never been much of a cookie eater," I said distinctly.

"What?" It was Maggie calling from the hall. "I'm home early. You've never been much of a what?"

"A cookie eater," I yelled at her. "I've never been one."

"No need to make an issue of it," Nelson said. "I believe you."

"I was just telling my wife," I told him.

"That's always best," he said. "I'll tell my wife. Is there anybody else you think ought to be told?"

"You bet," I told him. "If this community is going to the dogs, it's stupid jokers like you that have only themselves to blame. And one other thing—" I said. However, Mr. Nelson seemed to have hung up.

"What in the world was that all about?" Maggie was looking at me in amazement.

"That was the husband of your cookie woman," I told her. "He just got wise once too often."

"Oh no," she said. She grabbed the phone and started dialing. "I should have known something like this would happen—Hello

. . . Mrs. Nielson? I'm afraid there was a little mix-up. I know my husband didn't mean to call yours a stupid joker—"

I walked to the far end of the room and lit a cigarette. Nielson? That's what she said. I dropped the match into an ashtray. Not Nelson. Nielson.

Maggie was cradling the phone in both hands with a big artificial smile on her face. "He is?" she said. "In Toronto, you say? Well, there must have been some mistake." She threw me a murderous glance.

I left the house. If they wanted to make a border incident out of a few cookies, I wanted no part of it. I never did learn how it finally came out.

Then there was another time. Kit answered the phone. The call was for me, but she said I couldn't come because I was putting champagne into a washtub. Champagne happened to be the nitwit name of our dog that I was attempting to scrub. Kit had picked out the name because she thought it sounded classy.

How it sounded to my boss who had given me the day off to stay home and make out some reports was somewhat different. There was only one bright spot I could think of: I had managed to talk Kit out of naming the dog Brigitte Bardot.

Finally there was the incident last summer at the cottage. I had been lying on the beach killing time until four-thirty, when I was supposed to pick up Maggie at the station. My watch said three-ten. It had said three-ten the last time I'd looked. I had taken the watch away from Gretchen that morning when I caught her using it for the tiara of an Arabian queen in her sandbox. I gathered up my things and ran back to the cottage. The kitchen clock said four-twenty.

Gretchen and our neighbor Suzy were playing house in the bedroom.

"You girls run along," I told them. "I've got to get dressed and drive down to the station."

"We're playing house," Gretchen said. "Suzy's mother is taking a nap and she said Suzy was supposed to stay out of the house until she wakes up."

"That's fine," I said. "Now go on out."

They went into the living room and I started changing. I was just buttoning my shirt when the phone rang.

I listened, but it wasn't our ring. We were on a party line and it was for the cottage next door, it was for Suzy's house, as a matter of fact.

I called to her, "Suzy, that's your ring—if your mother's taking a nap maybe you'd better answer it."

She did and it was her father calling. "No," she said, "I can't call Mommy, because she's in bed and I'm not allowed to disturb her. There isn't any grownup here except Gretchen's daddy and he's going to the railroad station just as soon as he can get his clothes on." Then she hung up.

On our next vacation, we're going where there's no phone. In case of emergency just write me R.F.D.

And that's not all. Some of my most unnerving conversations have been with the company itself. A couple of weeks ago I got a call from a Miss Tuttle of the telephone company. She said my bill was overdue. I told her I'd look into it.

"When can we expect payment?" she asked.

"I don't know," I said. "My wife handles these things and she isn't here."

"Can we be sure of payment by the end of the week? Otherwise we will be forced to discontinue service."

Now I would like to say that Miss Tuttle has been calling me every month since she got the job three years ago. Before that her mother made the calls. So it wasn't like dealing with a stranger.

"You realize," she said, "I have nothing to do with it. It's company policy."

I suggested that maybe I could speak to somebody on the policy-making level. "Let's start with your boss," I said.

"You mean Mr. Asquith?"

"Asquith will be fine."

Miss Tuttle said, "Mr. Asquith is on vacation."

I said, "Who handles his work when he's away?"

Miss Tuttle said, "I do."

When my wife came home I told her about the call. "I paid

that bill last week," she said. "I gave it to you to mail. You put it in your briefcase."

I said, "I see." The next morning at the office I took the check out of my briefcase and put it in my coat pocket. It was a warm day and on the way home I left my coat at the cleaner's.

I didn't think any more about it until Saturday morning when Miss Tuttle called again. "Unless we receive payment by noon," she said, "we will have to discontinue service."

I said, "I can't get to your office before noon because my wife has the car. Besides she wrote you a check last week. She has the stub to prove it."

Miss Tuttle said she had no authority in such a matter.

I said, "Let me talk to somebody that does have authority. The district manager."

Miss Tuttle said, "There is no district manager."

I said, "There must be somebody in charge of the territory."

Miss Tuttle said, "The district supervisor is in charge."

I said, "Let me talk to the district supervisor."

Miss Tuttle said, "That would be Mr. Honeywell."

I said, "Let me talk to Mr. Honeywell."

Miss Tuttle said, "I'm sorry. That would be a toll call and we cannot allow toll charges on a delinquent account."

I said, "Miss Tuttle, don't play games with me. I don't want to know about company regulations. There is such a thing as the unwritten law."

"I can let you speak to Mr. Asquith," she said.

"He's on vacation."

"He came back yesterday," she said.

After a moment Mr. Asquith came on the line. "What can I do for you?" he asked.

I told him.

He said, "If you could arrange to settle the account on Monday I think we could make an exception this time."

"Mr. Asquith," I said, "I've been dealing with you people for twenty years, during that time you have sent me 240 bills and I've paid 239 of them. Now that I'm a few days late with the last bill you panic. That isn't the behavior of a healthy corporation."

"If you could make payment by Monday—"

I said, "Sears Roebuck doesn't go all to pieces when I'm a month or two behind. Neither does the May Company. When a firm the size of yours gets all worked up over a fifteen-dollar bill it must be in pretty shaky condition."

"Any time Monday," he said.

"Another thing," I said, "our phone cord is always getting snarled up. My wife and I are very careful about putting it back the same way we picked it up. It looks to me like you people are snarling it up from your end."

He said he'd look into it.

The following Saturday I happened to mention the incident to a friend of mine at a party. I said I would take it up with the president of the company if I knew who he was.

"Alfred Shuster is a member of the board," my friend said. "He lives right here in town. You could start with him."

It seemed like a good idea. As the evening went along it began to seem better and better. About eleven-thirty I phoned Shuster.

He asked what I wanted.

I said, "I guess you know that when a phone bill is overdue the company policy is to disconnect the phone."

"My God," he said, "don't you people ever sleep?"

"Perhaps I'd better explain—"

"Badgering customers just because their bill is a little overdue. I've always paid my bills before, what made you think I wasn't going to pay it this time?" His voice was becoming shrill and demanding. "You expect me to run out in the middle of the night when your office doesn't even open until Monday?"

I told him Monday would be fine.

"Another thing," he said, "this damned cord—"

I hung up gently. I hadn't gotten very far in solving my problem, but somehow I felt better. I wasn't alone any more.

The Old Familiar Booby Traps of Home

People tell me a lot of doctors won't make house calls these days. Ours does. He says he wouldn't miss them for the world.

The last time he came was on account of the suet. We had gotten a side of beef for the freezer and were having a hard time getting it all in. "I never dreamed there would be this much suet," Maggie said.

"The fellow ahead of me didn't want any of his," I said, "so I got a double portion. It's for the birds." Maggie just nodded.

I carried it out in the back yard and filled the feeders and put some in trees. There was about fifty pounds left. We have an above-ground pool with a four-foot platform next to it. I piled the suet on that.

The next day turned out to be a scorcher. Maggie called me at the office. "The suet's melting," she said. For such a simple remark it had an ominous sound.

"Tough luck for the birds," I said.

"There's not a bird in sight," she said. "I think they're afraid of the cats."

"We have cats?"

"Cats and dogs," she said. "No wolves yet, but somebody reported a pack of hyenas coming down Market Street."

When I got home the back yard sounded like an old Tarzan movie—snarling, spitting, growling. Cats in the feeders, cats in the trees, dogs on the pool platform.

I took off my jacket. "O.K.," I said to Maggie, "I'll get rid of them."

"The boys will be disappointed," she said, "they were going to sell tickets."

Two of the dogs on the platform started to fight. "That does it," I said. I turned on the hose and started forward. Anybody will tell you it's the only way to stop a dog fight.

"You should have turned the hose on them," the doctor said, "that's the only way to stop a dog fight." He opened his bag. "Where did you get bitten?"

"I didn't get bitten," I told him. "I wrenched my back picking up a Saint Bernard."

"A Saint Bernard?" he said. "My Lord, they run a hundred and fifty pounds."

"They weigh even more wet," I told him.

He looked thoughtful. "Can you tell me why anybody in his right mind would pick up a wet Saint Bernard?"

"Well," I said, "I couldn't think of any other way to get him out of the swimming pool."

While he was packing his bag he asked if I would mind giving a little talk at the next meeting of his medical society.

"What's the point?" I asked him. "I don't know anything about medicine."

"That's O.K.," he said. "I just want them to see you're real. They all think I've been making you up."

Then there was the time I got the severe stomach cramps. The doctor asked if I'd eaten anything out of the ordinary. I said I supposed it could have been the baby food.

"You've been eating baby food?" he asked.

Three jars I said. "I was trying to feed the baby but he wouldn't take it. The woman next door said I should take a spoonful myself and then give one to him. That was all right except that he kept spitting it out and I had to keep opening more jars."

"Did you eat anything else?"

"Yes, I had half a jar of dill pickles—to take away the taste of the baby food."

He told me some medicine I should take. "I don't guarantee it will do any good though. There were a lot of gaps in what they taught us in medical school and you seem to fall into most of them."

I've always liked natural decorations in a house—gourds and pussywillows, but you don't see them much any more. So when I brought home the armful of cattails, I was sure Maggie would be surprised. She was.

"They're for decorations," I explained. "You drape them over picture frames, put them in a vase, stand them in a corner." Maggie stood looking at them. "In the old days everybody did it."

"Probably grew them in a moat," she said.

I left them in the garage and a few weeks later I noticed they had gotten all puffy. I touched one and a whole cloud of fluff drifted down. A little later Maggie was looking out the front window. "What in the world," she said, "the air seems to be full of tan snow."

"It's just the boys," I said, "having a cattail fight."

"Oh no!" she said. "I just painted the front shutters."

We ran out, but it was too late. "The wind must have been just right," I said.

"All year we've had the worst-looking shutters in the neighborhood," she said, "now we've got mink."

She offered to phone the doctor, but I said I'd rather tell him myself. "I slipped on the back steps," I told him, "and sprained my ankle."

"Oh?" he said. "Who did you say was calling?"

"You know damned well who's calling."

49

"Then why don't you tell me what actually *did* happen?"

"All right. I fell off a ladder while I was scraping the shutters."

"Scraping the shutters," he said. "Getting ready to paint them?"

"They'd just been painted," I said.

"Just been painted," he said. "You decided you didn't like the color?"

"The color was fine," I said. "It was the texture. Too furry."

I could hear him saying something to his nurse. There was a kind of strangling sound and he came back on the line. "Furry shutters, eh? Well, that's more like it. For a minute there I thought I was talking to somebody else."

The time I burned my hand Maggie had taken my glasses in town to be fixed. We had gotten some tar all along one side of the car and I'd bought some special cleaner to take it off. There was a warning on the side of the can, but without my glasses I couldn't read the fine print. Now, I am nothing if not careful and I certainly wasn't going to use any product until I found out what the warning was. I brought a magnifying glass out from the house and held up the can where I could get good light on it.

As I discovered later, the warning said DO NOT EXPOSE TO HEAT. By then I already knew.

For some reason holidays have always been especially hazardous and I'm not talking about traffic accidents.

One Memorial Day I was at school helping out with the band and a kid shut his tuba case on my fingers.

Lots of people suffer from too much turkey on Thanksgiving. A couple of years ago I had twenty-five pounds too much. It was frozen and it fell off the shopping cart onto my foot.

Last Christmas Maggie was getting ready to make cookies when she discovered that Sammy had been using her favorite cookie cutter for Play Doh. It was caked all over it like concrete. She started to clean it, but I told her no—let Sammy do it. That's the only way to teach kids to take care of things.

Sammy said it was too hard, he couldn't wash it off. I told him to let it soak until it had softened. He did. In the bathtub. I didn't notice it until I sat down in the tub. It didn't make a very deep cut so for once I didn't have to call the doctor. Fortunately. I mean how do you explain a scar shaped like an angel?

One chore Maggie really hates is defrosting the freezer, so while she and the kids were away last July I decided to do it myself. It was the hottest day of the year and I figured all I had to do was wrap the food in newspaper and leave the lid up.

The trouble with a chest-type freezer is that the heat doesn't settle down into it to speak of. A fan is no help. I tried hot water, I tried salt, I tried a windshield scraper. Using the three together I began to get results. I scooped up the slush from the bottom and sloshed it on the sides. I used more water, more salt.

I was doing fine except that I kept dropping the scraper and dropping the bucket. I slapped my hands together but there was no feeling. It was like television with the sound turned up and the picture turned on but no set. I couldn't quit with a freezer half full of slush. By the time I was done, I was numb to the wrists.

I drove downtown very carefully. I didn't feel like explaining anything to some wise cop. It was bad enough explaining to the doctor.

"Ice, salt, water, and slosh it around," he said. "Do you realize what you've done? You've found the long-lost secret of ice cream?"

"Just get on with the treatment," I said. He told me to be patient.

"When you get something," he said, "you get it bad." I asked what he meant.

He tapped my hand. "Worst case of frostbite I've seen all summer."

You Know How It Is with Women

"I was figuring your wife would be here," the fellow said, "but you say she's gone out."

"You know how it is with women," I said, "here today, gone tomorrow." To tell the truth I was a little burned up at Maggie. She had gone downtown to get new school outfits for the kids, and not one damned word that she was expecting a repairman. I had figured that for once I'd have a Saturday afternoon to myself—take a nap—watch the ball game—whatever I wanted. And then this clown had showed up to fix the washer. I went ahead of him down the basement steps.

"My wife did mention that the washer wasn't working right, but I didn't know she'd called somebody to fix it."

"No? Well, like you say, that's how women are." He put his tool kit on the floor and switched on the machine. "Brother—the original Betsy Ross model." He fooled with the dial some more. "It could be worse, I guess, probably can patch it up so it'll run a little longer."

I lit a cigarette. "What do you mean—that's how women are?"

"Nothing personal, Mac." He pulled the washer out from the wall and started taking off the back. "You learn a lot about human nature in this business. Get so you can size up a person fast. Your wife was in my shop last week—we had a long talk."

"That was nice."

"Uh huh. I told her she ought to be on TV." He pried off the back of the machine and leaned it against the wall. "She said she'd thought some of going on the stage."

"Maggie told you that?"

"Didn't know about it, eh?" He nodded wisely. "You want to hand me the crescent wrench?" He pointed to his tool box. "It's that shiny thing on top."

"I know what a wrench looks like," I said. I handed it to him. "My wife did do some acting in school. The drama instructor said she ought to make it a career, but she never considered it seriously."

"Maybe not then." He had his head and shoulders inside the machine, kneeling on the wet floor. If he happened to touch a hot wire he'd really know it. Then I saw he'd pulled out the plug.

"What do you mean, not then?"

He moved back out of the washer. "Marriage doesn't always turn out like you think it's going to. Say your wife is here in the house and the kids are at school or taking a nap or some place like that. Maybe she's mopping the floor. Well, she gets to thinking—" he stopped poking inside the machine again. "You remember that old song?" and he began singing in an untrained and unpleasant tenor—

"She may be weary,
Women do get weary,
Wearing the same shabby dress—"

"O.K.," I said. "What do you expect her to wear while she's mopping the floor? An opera cape? Maggie has lots of good clothes."

"Knows how to wear them too. I noticed that right off."

I went over to the other end of the basement and stared out the window. I'd been looking forward to Saturday too. That's the trouble with having a repairman in the house. It doesn't do one bit of good to stand and watch him, but it's impossible to concentrate on anything else. It is for me anyhow—always has been.

I turned and walked back. "You find the trouble?" I asked.

"Wouldn't be surprised. These things get out of kilter sometimes, you know, just like everything else." He put down the wrench and picked up some pliers. "I remember one time a woman called me out to fix her washer. It was in awful shape. Turned out she'd used it to clean some clams. A whole bushel."

"What did she do that for?"

He shrugged. "Going to have a clambake I guess."

I put out my cigarette under the faucet of the wash tubs and laid it on the window sill. There were about half a dozen others. We never seem to have any ash trays around the basement.

"Yes," the man said for no reason I could see, "I was showing your wife a stove when she was in the other day. It's the latest deluxe model—all automatic. I wish you could have seen the look on her face."

"Yes," I said, "I'm sorry I missed it."

"She likes to cook you know. Said your favorite dessert was cherry cobbler."

I said, "Blueberry."

"Blueberry cobbler was it? Anyway she mentioned that she hadn't been able to do much baking lately. Sounds like the thermostat on your oven is shot."

"It's the oven door—it won't stay closed."

"Well, it doesn't matter. Like I always say a good cook deserves a good stove—a bad cook needs one." He glanced up at me. "You get it?"

"Look," I said, "as long as you're here why don't you fix the washer?"

He said, "That's what I'm doing."

I said, "Fine." I walked away. Over near the furnace there was a lot of broken glass on the floor along with some bolts and nails and so on. I had been looking for some staples a couple of days before in this jar and it had slipped out of my hand. I hadn't felt like cleaning it up at the time. Now I got a coffee can and started to salvage what I could. No sense in the afternoon being a total loss. Inside the washer Caruso had begun to sing again—

"She may be waiting—
Just anticipating
Things she may never possess—"

"Listen," I called to him, "my wife has as many appliances as any woman on the block. Mixer—blender—toaster—"

"She mentioned the toaster. Said half the time the toast doesn't pop up."

"Nothing's perfect," I said.

"I'll tell you what you do. You come down to the shop and pick out any toaster in the place. Bring it home and make a hundred slices of toast. If every single one doesn't pop up the toaster's yours. Free of charge."

"What the devil would I do with a hundred pieces of toast?" I asked him. I had just cut my thumb on a piece of glass. I went upstairs and put a bandage on it. That isn't easy to do with one hand.

When I got back downstairs the fellow was just stubbing out a cigarette on the floor. I picked it up and put it on the window sill with the others. He glanced up at the sill and then back at the floor and shook his head. He picked up a screwdriver.

"You go bowling much?" he asked me. "You and the wife?"

I had already answered the first part of his question by saying "fairly often" before he added the second part. Then I had to change it to "no."

"Maggie doesn't care much for bowling," I said.

"Uh huh." He started to hum the song again. It was the part in the middle where he tells about grief and care.

I banged my hand on the side of the machine until he stopped. "Now look," I said, "your little scheme isn't going to work, so you might as well give up. You're not going to con me into buying a lot of stuff I can't afford."

He gave me a puzzled look. "How's that again?"

"The way you keep hammering at me with that song," I said.

"Sure, I know most of our things are pretty beat up. I'd like to buy Maggie everything brand new, but right now it's out of the question."

He picked up the back plate and started to fasten it on the machine. "Tell me something—do you know the words to that song?" I nodded. "O.K. then. Can you tell me one place where it even mentions money?" I shook my head. "No, you can't. Tenderness, a little smile, things like that. Those are what's important to a woman." He got to his feet, plugged in the washer and turned it on. "There, listen to that—notice the difference?"

It sounded the same to me. "But all this sales talk you've been giving me—"

"I enjoy a little pleasant conversation," he said. "You get to know all different kinds of people. I didn't mean anything personal by it." He switched off the machine and began to wrestle it back to the wall. "As a matter of fact, I'll bet there isn't a washer on the block that couldn't use a little fixing up—a little adjusting."

"You may be right."

"I know I'm right." He slapped the lid of the washer and gave a little laugh. "You want to know the truth, my own washer at home is in worse shape than this one. The wife keeps after me to fix it, but I don't know—it seems like every time I get around to it there's something else—an emergency call—something." He started picking up his tools and putting them back in the kit. Then he got going on the song again, whistling this time. Our song. "A real catchy tune," he said. I nodded. "A lot of truth in it too." I followed him up the basement steps. They needed painting.

It was about an hour after he left when Maggie came home. I watched as she got out of the car—a fine-looking woman. You wouldn't be surprised to see her on any stage. I helped her carry in the packages and pile them on the couch. "It looks like an awful lot, doesn't it?" she said. "I'm afraid I spent more than I intended."

"Maggie," I said, "look at me." She did. "Maggie do you ever regret giving up a career on the stage?"

"What in the world—" Then she noticed the bandage. "You've hurt your thumb."

"A scratch," I said.

"You'd better let me look at it."

"You're evading the issue."

"There isn't any issue and you know it. I was never interested in a career."

"Not at the time maybe." I crossed the room and rested one elbow on the mantel, trying to get the most poignant effect from my lines. "But there must be dreary days—times when you consider the cooking, and the cleaning, the mending—and you think it might be different."

"Anybody can get tired of housework," she said, "there's no secret about that." She paused, eying me thoughtfully. "You wouldn't have been talking with Portia by any chance?"

"What does Portia have to do with it?"

"It's kind of a funny coincidence is all. She was saying just the other day that sometimes when the house and kids get too much for her she likes to imagine she's a famous actress—steeped in luxury and all that. So then I admitted I did too. I expect most women do sometime or other. It's just daydreaming—it doesn't mean anything."

"I see." I decided this part of the conversation had gone far enough. "You know that new play that just opened at the Colony, how'd you like to see it tonight?"

I had expected this would get a reaction and it did. But only for a moment. She sighed. "It would be wonderful," she said, "but we wouldn't get tickets this late. Besides I've already shot the budget for this month." She came over and brushed my hair back with her fingers. "It was sweet of you to think of it anyway."

"I've already arranged for the tickets. And I've reserved a table at Pierre's."

She stared at me for a moment in a state of shock. Then she put her arms around my neck. "I don't know what crime you're trying to cover up," she said, "but whatever it is it's worth it."

"You know," I said after a minute, "if things had worked out differently I might be taking my wife downtown tonight to see you on the stage. I like it this way better."

Maggie said, "You and me." She stepped over and picked up a package from the couch. "Look, why don't you fix us a drink while I take this over to Portia? It's a blouse I exchanged for her."

I said, "I thought she was going to meet you downtown."

"She was, but then she remembered the man was coming to fix her washer so she had to stay and wait for him."

I said, "He was supposed to fix Portia's washer?"

"That's what I just said. Apparently he's a real weird character. Portia said she stopped by his shop only intending to stay a minute and she was there an hour. He practically talked her arm off." She glanced out the window. "I was hoping I could get a look at him—you didn't notice if he was there did you?"

I said, "Maggie, I think there's something you ought to know."

She raised her eyebrows. "There is?"

I took her by the hand and led her over to the easy chair. I sat down and pulled her onto my lap. She was looking at me expectantly.

"This fellow who was supposed to fix Portia's washer did show up," I said. "Only he showed up here. He fixed our washer."

Maggie said, "That's impossible."

"It does seem that way, doesn't it? But you know I've said all along those fancy numbers you got for the house are impossible to read."

"Didn't he even ask your name?"

"He called me Mac. Said he'd come to fix the washer. Well, you had mentioned that it wasn't working right."

Maggie started to laugh. She rested her head on my shoulder and laughed until she was shaking. I started to laugh too. Finally she sat up and wiped her eyes. "Poor Portia. I guess I'd better go break the news." She started to get up.

I pulled her back, "What's the rush?"

She snuggled against me. "Well, now that you mention it—" After a moment she chuckled. "It's mean to laugh, but when I think of his coming to the wrong house—"

I tightened my arms around her. "He came to the right house," I said.

The Chick Chick Syndrome

Maggie has always been like a kid about holidays—Thanksgiving, Christmas—she can hardly wait. That's why I was so surprised when she remarked that she was dreading Easter.

"How can you say that?" I asked. "Aside from the religious significance it means the end of winter. It's a time of budding and blooming—a fresh start for all."

"It's also a time for coloring eggs, for hiding eggs, for fighting over eggs, for stepping on eggs. And I haven't even mentioned the candy—a chick chick here, a bunny bunny there—"

I took her by the arm and sat her on the couch. "Maggie," I said, "you shouldn't keep your problems bottled up, you should bring them out, share them."

"Share what?" she asked. "Easter eggs are a pain in the neck, that's all."

"It probably goes back to your childhood," I explained, "the little girl next door got a big decorated egg and you didn't. You felt rejected."

"My father was an Easter egg fanatic," she said, "we were still eating them on Memorial Day."

"How the devil do you expect me to work out your emotional problems if you won't co-operate?" I asked. "Now this hatred of Easter eggs."

"I don't hate anything," she said. "I just don't like the confusion and the fighting. It's as simple as that."

"Very well, this year I'll take over the whole operation."

"Maybe it isn't as simple as that," she said.

I knew she was expecting me to make a botch of it, so I made up my mind to fool her. Saturday afternoon when Maggie came into the kitchen I had the eggs boiled and the dye mixed, newspapers spread over the table, the decorations all laid out and everything spotless. I opened the freezer, took out two bloody marys, and handed her one. "I know you like them extra cold," I said.

She shook her head. "I simply can't believe it."

I smiled. "Sorry to disappoint you." I picked up an egg carton from the shelf. "I had a dozen left over," I said, "you want to put them in the refrigerator?"

She reached for the carton and I let go of it a split second too soon. She lunged and missed it. "Damn it."

I picked it up, laughing. "It was only an empty carton."

Maggie set her glass on the table. It was empty too. The bloody mary was spread from the neck of her dress all the way to the hem. "A little joke," I explained. She didn't say anything, just stood there staring at me. And dripping. I picked up her glass. "I'll mix you another," I said, "I hope I can get it cold enough."

She turned very slowly and started out of the room. "The last one was just right," she said.

I wiped up the floor and called in the kids. I put Roy and Gretchen on one side of the table and Sammy on the other. He's the youngest and needs the most room. There were eight colors and I gave Gretchen and Sammy three each and Roy two because he was oldest.

Roy said that was no fair—he always had to give in because he was oldest. There was a certain amount of truth in that so I took one bowl from each of the others. They set up a howl about that. "I don't want to hear another sound from you," I said. "Shut up and dye."

Sammy wanted to know why the Easter Bunny hid the eggs instead of putting them in your stocking. I said I didn't know. Gretchen wanted to know if he had a wife and I said I didn't know.

Sammy asked if there had been an Easter Bunny when I was a kid. I said sure. "Wow," he said, "I never knew rabbits got that old."

He started to move the purple dye over to his side, and Gretchen grabbed it and tried to pull it away from him. "Stop it! I said. "Let go of that bowl!" Sammy did.

Gretchen started to cry. "Never mind," I told her, "it's only vegetable dye and you have to take a bath anyway. It'll wash out of your dress." I got the orange dye from the shelf and gave her that to keep it even.

She said it was all Sammy's fault. He said it was her own fault— she should have let go when I told her to. Roy said they both better shut up.

"That's enough," I said. "If you don't quit this the Easter Bunny won't bring you any eggs."

"Who cares?" Roy said. "We already got the eggs."

"Well then, he'll hide them so good you won't find them."

"I think that's plain mean," Gretchen said. "The Easter Bunny makes me sick."

"Oh he does?" I said. "Well, let me tell you Miss Smarty Pants, you make the Easter Bunny sick."

"What did you say?" Maggie had just come in wearing a fresh outfit.

Roy looked up. "He said Miss Smarty Pants here would make the Easter Bunny sick."

She nodded. "That's what I thought he said, but I couldn't believe it." Then she happened to notice Gretchen. "Well, well," she said, "he worked it on you too."

"An accident," I said.

She picked up the bowl from the shelf. "How come you're not using the green dye?"

"That would make an uneven number," I said, "three wouldn't go into it."

Maggie said, "Three *is* an uneven number."

"Look," I said, "who's in charge this year?"

"I'm sorry," she said, "this year three *isn't* an uneven number." Women have no head for figures.

Easter morning Maggie took the kids to church while I stayed home to hide the eggs and candy. Maggie had about thirty pounds hidden in the closet and I counted everything in multiples of three. I put it all into a big basket and took it out in the yard. After a while Hubie Marlow came over from across the street. "Hiding Easter eggs?" he asked. I don't answer questions like that. "The reason I ask," he went on, "is because if that's what you think you're doing you're wrong. I can see a dozen from here."

"I've already used up all the hiding places," I said, "and I still have six chocolate bunnies, twelve marshmallow chickens, twenty-four candy eggs—"

"How about blindfolding the kids?"

"Easter is early this year," I said, "and the weeds haven't come up yet. Another couple of months and I could hide a bushel of eggs."

"There's an answer for everything," Hubie said. He went into the garage and came out with a stack of empty flowerpots. He started putting them upside down on the grass.

"You call those hiding places?" I asked. "That's the first place they'll look."

"You don't put an egg under each one," he said, "that's the secret." Some secret. By the time I'd finished with the pots Hubie had brought out the bikes and sleds, tools, paint cans—

"Hubie," I said, "don't you think the yard is beginning to look a little tacky?"

He brought out some bundles of old newspapers. "Do you want your children to have a happy Easter or not? It's as simple as that." I shrugged. "I'll need help with the rowboat," he said.

Hubie had just left when Maggie drove in. The kids jumped out yelling, and ran in for their baskets. Maggie stood looking around thoughtfully. "I had to make some extra hiding places," I explained. She didn't answer. People were strolling home from church in all their finery. They all slowed down as they passed the house. The Easter Parade. "I think your new bonnet looks great," I said. Maggie nodded and walked away.

When the kids had found all the eggs and candy I asked them if they wouldn't like to help carry all the things into the garage.

"The Easter Bunny got it out," Sammy said, "let him put it back." I started picking up flowerpots.

In a little while Maggie came out to the garage.

She was wearing slacks and carrying a couple of bloody marys. "Here," she said, "sit down and relax and then I'll give you a hand."

I sat down on the wheelbarrow. "You're not mad at me?"

"At the Easter Bunny?" She grinned. "How could I?"

"I've been wondering about the kids," I said. "Do you suppose they really believe in him?"

"They'd better," she said, "if it weren't for him they wouldn't be here."

"Maggie—" I hesitated.

"Uh huh," she said, "but let's clean up the yard first."

So we did. And if anybody is still wondering if the Easter Bunny has a wife, the answer is yes.

One of the best.

Promissory Note

If you ever have occasion to sign a contract, somebody is sure to warn you to read the fine print. But nobody ever warns you about making a promise. And a promise is all fine print.

The most important difference is that a good lawyer can break a contract. Promises, having no legal standing, are irrevocable. They are the invisible cords that draw humanity together in a single lump. In many households promises are used as a medium of exchange like wampum. When they play "Oh, Promise Me" at weddings it's not just because it has a catchy tune.

A fellow I knew, Arnie Becker, mortgaged his whole future with a careless promise. During their honeymoon at a lakeside resort, his bride, Dolores, happened to admire a beautiful motorboat and Arnie promised to get her one just like it some day.

She asked if he really meant it, and Arnie, whose mind was on other things, said sure. Later when he objected to paying six hundred dollars for some living-room furniture, Dolores asked him how much a boat would cost. Arnie figures that so far that one promise has cost him a blond wig, wall-to-wall carpeting, and a vacation in Bermuda for his mother-in-law, besides the furniture. And the price of boats keeps going up. Now the thing is Dolores doesn't actually want that boat, she'd rather have the promise. That's what pays the dividends.

There are two basic types of promises, only one of which is dangerous. The morning after or I'll-never-do-that-again is quite harmless because you aren't going to keep it and nobody expects you to.

It's when you're feeling good that you have to be on guard. On a Saturday evening for example, you may be feeling relaxed and your judgment isn't quite as keen as it seems to be. You are feeling self-confident, affectionate, sentimental. Nostalgia is beginning to set in.

These are nature's warning signals. This is when you must establish a negative frame of mind. Whatever anybody asks you tell him no. You may get the reputation of being a grouch, but don't let it bother you. It's better than waking up on Sunday morning and finding you've promised to give a talk on good citizenship to the Campfire Girls.

Children are especially good at trapping you into promises. Turn them down and they ask you again. People tend to think of children as impatient. The fact is their patience is relentless. What adult could stand to ask for something a hundred times without stopping? It doesn't bother a kid. He knows who's going to crack first.

A while ago Roy asked me when I was going to sleep out in the tent with him. I told him not to be ridiculous.

"But you promised," he said.

"That was last July," I said, "this is November."

"After all," Maggie said, "you did promise."

I settled for taking Roy and two of his friends to a model car exhibition and a Disney double feature.

I don't want to give the impression that I'm not in favor of children. I realize that they are what gives spice and flavor to our lives. As the father of six once remarked, "A home without children is like a cut finger without salt."

It may be significant that stories for children are so often involved with promises—the more indiscreet and hare-brained the better. For instance there's the princess locked up in a tower full of flax which she has to spin before she can get out. And when some troll shows up and offers to spin it if she'll promise to marry him, she says sure. Princesses in fairy tales hardly ever say no to anything. Come to think of it, keeping them locked up in towers may not have been a bad idea.

Kings in those days didn't have to take a back seat either when it came to idiotic promises. They were always offering their daughter's hand and half their kingdom to anybody who could answer three questions. Why they chose that particular method to dispose of their property is anybody's guess. But they all did it. Probably one of the reasons there aren't many kingdoms any more.

Nobody is immune to promise making—not even poets. I think Robert Frost sums it up best. He describes stopping by the woods one evening to watch the snow come down. No doubt it's been another long, tough day and now he'd just like to sit for a while and do nothing. But, he says, he has promises to keep. Maybe he's agreed to help put up booths for the church bazaar, or clean out his desk, or go and look at somebody's home movies. He never tells us. All we know is that he has miles to go and these damned promises waiting for him. I've had the same feeling a thousand times.

For some reason big promises aren't nearly as troublesome as small ones. You promise the bank you'll pay them so much a month and there's no problem. You don't pay them—they take your house.

It's the little promises that eventually weigh you down—the ones there's no way of getting out of. People ask you to do things and you agree. They tell you to come back in six months and have your teeth checked and to return the lemons whenever you're passing by and to let them know the name of that piano tuner when you get a chance. So you promise.

None of these things have a deadline. A few days one way or

the other won't make any difference. But after a year or so they begin to get on your nerves. You move your tongue around the tooth the filling has fallen out of. You feel pretty sure the people have found another piano tuner by this time. But suppose they haven't? What if they're still waiting?

And the people you borrowed the lemon from—the last time you saw them did they seem a little distant? Did they make a point of avoiding the subject? One thing is sure—you can't return two lemons you borrowed fourteen months before. It's psychologically impossible.

Sooner or later you're going to have to go back to the dentist and you know he's going to have quite a few words about all those cavities. You may like to try my system—before I went back to see him I went to a strange dentist for some emergency repairs. The only trouble was I had to promise him to come back in six months.

It doesn't seem fair somehow. We can be forgiven for our sins and pardoned for our crime. But our promises are with us forever —the eternal sand in the bathing suit of life.

Probably the most exasperating promises are the ones that are the most meaningless. Like people asking you to look up some friend of theirs. I always say sure. More than likely there's a princess somewhere among my ancestors.

Once when we were passing through the town of Moon Lake, Maggie reminded me that I had promised a drunk at a party that if I was ever there I would look up Frank and Alma Cleever and tell them Harry Andrews said hello. "A promise is a promise," she added somewhat unnecessarily.

I finally located the house about eight miles out of town. A large collie came bounding out of the house followed by a little girl who said her father was back by the barn. I followed her around the house with the collie following me in a series of short lunges.

Mr. Cleever was sitting astride the ridge pole of the barn with a hammer in his hand. He was about thirty feet from the ground. "Mr. Cleever?" I called up to him.

He put his hand behind his ear and yelled back something I

couldn't make out. The dog was barking continuously. I shook my head.

He laid down the hammer and started backing cautiously down the roof. "Never mind!" I yelled. I turned to the little girl. "Tell him not to bother." She moved back a step. Mr. Cleever had caught his pants leg on a nail about halfway down.

"Forget it," I called, "go on back." He got loose from the nail, crawled over to the ladder and came down to the ground.

He inspected the torn knee of his pants and then looked at me. "Yeah?" he said.

I smiled. "Mr. Cleever, I was talking to a friend of yours— Harry Anderson."

He said, "Who?"

"Andrews I mean—Harry Andrews."

He said, "What about him?"

I said, "I promised him I'd stop and say hello."

He said, "I see."

I nodded. He looked at me, not saying anything. "Well," I said, "that's about it," and turned and walked back to the car.

I realize this doesn't sound like much of a story, but sometimes at night I wake up and think about it. Usually I don't get back to sleep for an hour or more.

What we need, I think, is a national holiday to mark the termination of all promises. We could call it Cancellation Day. There wouldn't be any parades or speeches. People across the land could relax for the first time, relieved of their burden of foolish promises. It would be a day of quiet rejoicing and firm resolve. I know that if I could ever wipe the slate clean I'd never get hooked again. That's a promise.

Homework

At the school the boys go to the honor roll is divided into Outstanding Scholarship, Honors Scholarship, and Honorable Mention. We were visiting some friends one evening not long ago and I happened to remark that Roy had made Honorable Mention.

"Yeah," Al said, "the same thing happened to Curtis a few months back. There was no TV for him for some time, I can tell you that."

This struck me as being slightly irrational, until finally it came out that this was the first time Curtis hadn't made Outstanding Scholarship. Big deal. As I said to Maggie on the way home, if there's one thing I can't stand it's parents who brag about their kids' grades.

"From now on," I said, "I'm going to go over their homework with the boys every night—until they get straightened out."

I told Roy that we'd have to work on his spelling. "When I was your age I was almost always first or second in the spelling bees."

He wanted to know what that was. I said when people would get together to do something special they called it a bee. "You mean like a party?" he asked.

"You might call it a party," I said. I explained about spelling bees, husking bees, and so on. Later I overheard him talking to Sammy.

"You know what they used to do when Dad was a boy?" he asked. "When they wanted to have a party? They got a lot of people together and pulled the husks off corn and spelled hard words."

"Man," Sammy said, "no wonder he gets crabby so often."

The first evening I thought I'd see what they knew about history. "What can you tell me about George Washington?" I asked.

"He went across the river standing up," Sammy said, "and he chopped down the cherry tree."

"It didn't really happen," Roy said. "It's just a lie somebody made up to teach kids to tell the truth."

"That's right," I said, "children have to learn that lies never do any good."

"That one never did anyhow," Sammy said.

"How about Columbus?" I asked. He was an old-time discoverer they said. That was about it. "He was a great man," I said. "The King of Spain made him a knight with golden spurs for his discoveries." I told about all his voyages, how he thought he had discovered China. "He wanted to prove you could reach the East by sailing west."

"That's dumb," Roy said. "It's like walking around the block to go next door."

"Or walking around the house to get to the kitchen," Sammy said.

"That's enough," I told them. "You can stop acting so smart. I'll bet Columbus never got a D in social studies."

"Yeah," Sammy said, "but I'll bet he never had Mrs. Hazeltine either."

"Let's stick to the subject," I said. "His crew were scared because they thought the sea was flat and when the ship got to the edge it would go right over."

Sammy said he didn't believe it. "No," Roy said, "nobody would believe that. If the ship went over the edge, the water would too. There wouldn't be any sea."

"We know that," I said, "but they didn't. They had no idea the world was round."

"Makes no difference," Sammy said, "you pour water on a table and it will run over the edge. Same with the ocean."

"Right," said Roy, "can't you see that? If the water kept pouring over the edge all those years where would it go?"

"I didn't say it went anywhere," I said.

"It would have to," Sammy said, "and that's the reason a flat world won't work."

"Okay," I said, "now what can you tell me about Columbus?"

"Well," Roy said, "he made the king give him spurs for sailing his boat. He thought America was China, so he called the people Indians and on the way home he sank the *Santa Maria*."

"Yup," said Sammy, "and for this they named a day after him."

"That's enough history for now," I told them.

The boys didn't have much trouble with math except for the word problems. "Let's try one," I said. "Now, forty-two Scouts are going to a ball game in seven cars. How many Scouts to a car? Sammy, you mean to tell me you can't divide seven into forty-two?"

He said sure but how can you divide cars into Scouts? His teacher kept telling them you can't subtract apples from pears. He wasn't subtracting, I said, he was dividing and that was different. He said maybe it would work with cars but not with buses. I told him not to be ridiculous. He kept insisting. "All right," I said, "give me a problem and we'll try it."

He said 393 kids were going to the game and they had 20 buses. How many to each bus? "Fine," I said. "Twenty goes into 39 once. Nought from 9 is 9—" Sammy said hold it.

"The 20 is buses and the 393 is kids. You can't subtract."

I looked at the paper. The kid was right. You try to subtract buses from kids and what do you wind up with? I picked up my pencil and went on with the problem. "It comes out to 19 to a bus with 13 left over."

Sammy stared at me. "You mean those 13 kids don't get to go?"

"I didn't say that."

Roy said probably their mothers would take them. Sammy said that wasn't fair if all the rest got to go by bus. Roy said what if they rented another bus? It took me a minute to figure it. "That would make 18 in a bus with 15 over."

"It keeps getting worse," Roy said.

Sammy said he thought arithmetic was a lousy, crummy subject. "And long division is the worst."

"You can't blame it on arithmetic," I said, "it's doing the best it can." Sammy said that wasn't good enough.

But later after he'd gone to bed he came back down to tell me he'd got it figured out. "All you have to do is borrow seven kids from another problem."

One afternoon I was looking through Roy's science book and decided to try some of the experiments. The first was on the reflection of light. I had the boys pull down all the living-room shades except one at the side with the sun coming in. Then I put a big piece of green paper down in the sunlight. I was starting to explain why this made everything in the room look green, when a girl came to the door. She was collecting money for some outfit called the Zero Population Growth Society. I invited her in.

She seemed nervous, flighty. "Are you all right?" she asked. "You don't look very well." I told her I'd never felt better. "You're kidding," she said. She looked around kind of uneasy. "Look—let's forget the population growth—okay?"

The boys came out of the gloom to say hello. "Oh my God," she said, "they've got the same thing!" I tried to explain, but she was out the door. She didn't look back.

After that I showed them the principle of the windlass, using the pencil sharpener on the kitchen wall. I ran a cord from the end of the sharpener to a scrub bucket on the floor and showed them how to lift the bucket by turning the crank. Roy said big deal lifting an empty bucket. I said okay, we'll use a full one. Sammy started to fill it with water but I put a stop to that. "Find something that won't make a mess if it spills." Roy put a stack of cookbooks in it and Sammy put in a big bunch of bananas. It added up to a pretty good weight.

Roy started to turn the crank, the cord grew taut, the bucket shifted and the pencil sharpener came off the wall. "Hey," Sammy said, "it works."

"Yeah," Roy said, "only how often do you want to take down a pencil sharpener?"

"You don't get the idea," I said. I got some heavier screws and fastened it back more securely. This time it worked fine. I left the boys taking turns with it. After a minute Sammy called me to come back and see their invention. I went over to take a closer look. He had the bucket cranked up as high as it would go and was just holding it there. "So—what is it?"

"A power pencil sharpener," Roy said. He shoved a pencil in it and Sammy let go the crank.

When Maggie got home from the store she wanted to know who my visitor had been. I said there hadn't been any. "Oh?" she said. "Ella Randall said she was driving by and saw some girl coming out the front door."

"Yes," I said. "Well, that must have been the one from the Zero Population Growth people."

"I see," she said. "Ella wondered why all the living room shades were down."

"The shades," I said. "I suppose a person might wonder about that." I limped over to the sink to get a drink. "You see I was showing the boys a science experiment." After I'd explained she still looked at me sort of funny. "Look," I said, "ask the boys if you don't believe me."

"Oh I believe you," she said. "Who cares what the neighbors think?" She started taking the groceries out of the bags. "What happened to your foot? The boys tried to tell me you hurt it on an automatic pencil sharpener."

It was another experiment, I told her, and a bucket fell on it. An empty bucket? she asked. No, I said. A full one. She went on putting groceries away. Full of what? she asked. This and that I said. Uh huh, she said. This and that what? Sawdust? Coal? Cookbooks and bananas, I said. She stopped what she was doing and looked at me for a minute. She shook her head. "These days you aren't even safe in your own home," she said.

I went over to help with the groceries. "Do you suppose there's such a thing as giving the boys too much help?" she asked. "I mean, make them too dependent?"

I studied a box of cereal. "Maggie," I said, "you know what I think I'll do? I think I'll teach the boys to stand on their own two feet—think for themselves. I'm going to let them do their own homework just like my father always let me do mine."

She nodded slowly. "It's the American way," she said.

The 32nd of March

April Fools' Day is not what it used to be, in my opinion. I don't
think people really understand it. Maggie says, what's to understand? Well, for one thing there are two kinds of jokes—good to
bad and vice versa. The first is when somebody offers you a piece
of candy (good) and it turns out to be chocolate-covered soap
(bad). The second is when somebody tells you something terrible
has happened (bad) and after you've stewed for a while they say
April Fool (good).

"This is your idea of a joke?" Maggie asked. "Telling somebody
his wife has run off with the garbage man?"

"Of course not," I said, "it has to be something believable."

"Oh? Tell that to Karl Beckenbach. Or maybe you'd better
not."

"Who's this?"

"The man that has the electric repair shop—you know. His wife

75

ran off with the garbage man—well, it must be almost a year ago now. That's what made me think of it."

"That still doesn't mean the next fellow will believe it, just because it happened to—what did you say his name was?"

"Beckenbach," she said, "the tall, skinny fellow."

"And it happened a year ago? Funny I never heard about it."

"April Fool," she said.

"That's not fair," I said. "April Fools' Day isn't until next week."

"I like to do mine early," she said. "Besides, you said it wasn't believable and you believed it."

I don't think any woman really appreciates April Fools' Day. They don't have the temperament. "It's got to be on the right day," I said, "or there's no point."

"That's what I say, it's a dumb idea anyhow."

"It's a fine old American tradition," I said. I called the boys in. "Next Thursday is April Fools' Day," I said, "have you two made your plans?" They just looked at each other.

"You're supposed to play tricks on people—jokes."

Roy held up his fist. "See my fingers? See my thumb? You're dumb." Sammy went off into gales of laughter. It looked like I had my work cut out.

"The point is to catch the other fellow," I said. "For instance you phone the drugstore and ask if they have Prince Albert in the can. When the man says yes, you say why don't you let him out?" The boys were staring at me blankly. "Prince Albert is a kind of tobacco," I said, "comes in a can."

"That's an April Fool joke?" Sammy asked.

"One of the better ones," Maggie said.

"Or you call somebody and ask if his house is on the streetcar line. When he says yes you say well, you better get out, there's a streetcar coming."

Roy wanted to know what a streetcar line was. I said tracks like railroad tracks.

"You mean people used to build their houses on them?" Sammy asked.

I said of course not, they built them the same place they do now. Roy said, "You mean the streetcars came right up in the yard?"

I don't know. Sometimes I have the feeling that children today have no sense of humor at all. "Another thing you can do is put a hat on the sidewalk and when somebody comes along and kicks it there's a brick under it and he stubs his toe."

The three of them looked at each other. "Why does he kick the hat?" Roy asked.

"It's human nature," I said. "You see a hat on the sidewalk and you want to kick it."

Sammy said he'd never seen a hat on the sidewalk. Neither had the others. "You've seen it in the comics, haven't you?" I said. "George Bungle, Tillie the Toiler, Andy Gump? Doesn't anybody read the funnies any more?"

Roy wanted to know where you would get a brick. People already had them I said. "We've got a whole stack in back of the garage."

Maggie shook her head. "No we don't. Your father had a stack in back of his garage, but that was twenty years ago."

"Let's not dwell in the past," I said. I told them about the pocketbook on a string, and the chocolate soap and all the other old favorites. The one they liked best was the mouse. I showed them how to bend a paper clip into a horseshoe and put a rubber band across with a button threaded on it. Then you wind up the button and put it in an envelope to hold it flat. When somebody opens it, the button spins, making a noise like a mouse trying to get out and scares the pants off them.

"Now remember," I said, "these things may work now, but on April Fools' Day everybody is going to be on guard, so you have to be extra tricky."

The boys looked thoughtful for the first time. Maybe there was some hope.

When I got home Thursday I found a wallet by the garage door. There was a cord tied to it and going around the corner. It was so clumsy and obvious it was sort of touching.

"Well," I said, "what's this—a wallet?" I peered around the corner. The cord ran up over the edge of the roof. There was a ladder just beyond it. I climbed up until I could see over the edge. The cord was fastened to a pan of water. "Clever," I said, "very clever. But not quite clever enough."

When I got down to the ground I discovered that the back of the upper rungs had been freshly painted—red on the left, blue on the right. I found some turpentine in the garage to clean my hands and went in the house.

Maggie said the boys were out playing April Fool jokes. "They seemed to think you expected it."

I hung up my jacket and took my paper into the living room. I noticed that the candy dish contained four very dubious-looking chocolates.

It wasn't long before the boys came in. They said all the kids were out playing jokes on each other and nothing worked very well. "Like this—" Roy held out the wallet. "There was a string tied to it, but nobody pulled it away like you said."

"And it had two dollars in it," Sammy said. "Who would play a trick like that?"

I looked over to where Maggie was looking at a magazine. "Somebody pretty devious," I said. To myself I added that that was a game that two could play.

"I almost forgot," I said, "I got tickets for the ice show on Saturday. They're in the pocket of my jacket. If you'd like to just reach in the breast pocket and bring them here. I thought you might enjoy it. However, if you'd rather not—what's this?" Roy had his hand held out.

"The tickets," he said.

"Well, great," I said. "It's April first, doesn't that mean anything to you? If somebody asks you to do something that seems odd, that should sound a warning. There could have been anything in that pocket—pins, a mousetrap—anything."

"What was in it?" Maggie asked.

"Just the tickets," I said, "that was the point. The boys should have suspected something fishy and refused to reach in. Then I would have taken out the tickets and said okay I'll take somebody else. That was the trick."

Maggie frowned at Roy. "What was the idea anyhow? Ruining Dad's trick?"

"It's not that," I said. "I'm just disappointed that he wasn't more alert."

Sammy asked if I'd show him how to make a mouse again. "You weren't paying attention," I said, "it's really very simple." I showed him how to bend the paper clip, thread the button on the rubber band, and wind it up. "Now if you'll get me an envelope to put it in—" I opened the envelope and found there was already a mouse in it.

Maggie came running in from the kitchen. "What is it?" she asked. "What happened?"

"Nothing," I said, "the boys just played an April Fool trick."

"Well," she said, "isn't that what you wanted?"

"Of course it is," I said. "It's exactly what I wanted. Now if you'll all just let me get back to my paper—"

Sammy passed me the candy dish. I said no thanks. "You sure?" Maggie said. "You always liked chocolates."

"I also like horseback riding," I said, "but I don't happen to feel like it at the moment."

"Okay," she said. She took a piece and bit into it. The boys each took a piece.

"Man," Sammy said, "this is good." The three of them stood there chewing and looking at me.

"All right," I said, "let me tell you where you made your mistake. The candies looked very funny—a little *too* funny in fact. I was supposed to think there was something wrong and not take any. But I didn't fall for it—I just pretended to be fooled to see how far you'd go."

They exchanged sheepish looks. "If you expect to fool an old dog with new tricks—" The phone rang, and for once neither boy moved to answer it—a giveaway right there. I went over and picked up the receiver.

"Hello," the woman said, "do you have Prince Albert in the can?" Her voice sounded strangely like Maggie's sister's.

"Why, yes," I said innocently, "we certainly do."

"How much is it?" she asked, "the one-pound can?"

"How much?" I said. "Well, I'm not sure."

She said, "This is Vogel's Pharmacy, isn't it?"

"Why no," I said, "this is a private residence."

"Really?" she said. "How do you happen to carry tobacco?"

"We don't," I said, "but you see today is April Fools' Day—"

"And you wanted to play a trick—"

"No, no," I said, "I thought you were playing one—you see I thought you were somebody else."

"Oh? People often do."

"I thought you were a relative of my wife's." She didn't say anything. "You're not, are you?"

"I couldn't say," she said. "I don't even know who your wife is."

I said it wasn't important and hung up. Maggie was staring at me. "Wrong number," I said. There was something about the way Maggie looked. "You wouldn't happen to know anything about it, would you?"

"What's to know about a wrong number?"

I said skip it. Going back to my chair, I took the last of the candies. It was chocolate-covered soap.

Power Play

Everybody worries about the energy crisis, but I sort of like it. For one thing it is now considered smart to save electricity. Patriotic even.

As I said to Maggie, "I hope you realize that I was patriotic long before anybody else. All those years when everybody was calling me cheap."

She said she would see about getting a star for my desk.

"Let's try to do even better," I said. "I'm not asking for any sacrifices—use all the electricity you want, but let's not waste it."

Maggie said she'd do all she could. "We can disconnect the doorbell when we go out," she said. "And when I listen to the radio, I won't tune in any out-of-town station."

I knew she meant well. "I guess what bothers me most is the idea of some utility company getting rich off of us."

"Really?" she said. "I'll have to keep an eye on them. If anybody can get rich off of us, I want to see how they do it."

It was about this time that I got hold of a book on how to save energy. It was a real eye-opener. For example, one leaking hot-water faucet can waste forty dollars a year. "Do you realize how many we have?" I asked Maggie. "Counting tubs, showers, and the rest? Seven. At forty dollars a year that would be two hundred and eighty dollars we could save for a few pennies' worth of washers." I went down cellar for my wrench. In a few minutes I was back.

"Finished already?" Maggie asked.

I picked up my book. "The roof leaks," I said. "The basement leaks, the hose leaks. The hot-water faucets do not leak. Not a single blasted one."

"Isn't that good?"

"In a way, yes," I said. "Only I'd been counting on saving that two hundred and eighty bucks. I thought we might even be able to take a little trip."

"Keep reading," she said.

"You can forget about my razor and the waffle iron and corn popper. They wouldn't save us enough to drive around the block."

Maggie said that was okay. "We've already driven around the block," she said, "don't you remember? I think it was our seventh anniversary. Seven is asphalt, isn't it?"

"Ditto the sewing machine," I said. "You could use it twice as much, make yourself twice as many clothes, and still keep under a dollar."

"Yes," she said, "but then I'd only have to get another hanger."

Heaven knows I want my family to enjoy all modern conveniences, but the other morning at breakfast I couldn't help noticing: Kit had turned on the oven to warm her cereal bowl, Roy left the refrigerator open while he went out to pour milk for the cat, Sammy turned on the disposal for three orange seeds and Maggie put an ice cube in her coffee.

I gave a little chuckle. "I noticed you put an ice cube in your coffee," I remarked.

"Heh, heh, heh," she said, "it was too hot."

"And what made it too hot?" I held up a finger. "Electricity. The same thing that made the ice cube cold."

Sammy said he didn't see how that would work. I told him to eat his cereal. He said he wanted a banana on it. Roy said bananas came from Central America—they'd studied it. Sammy said he had too—bananas, chewing gum, and canals. Kit said she'd gotten gum on her green skirt.

Speaking of ice cubes in coffee, I said, it didn't make sense electricitywise. Maggie said that was how she liked it. Like turning up the electric blanket and opening a window, I said, the pointless conflict of heat and cold. She said I liked ice cream with hot fudge sauce. Anybody could see the difference there, I said. About 450 calories, she said—600 with whipped cream and nuts. I said possibly she considered my point trivial. She said no, she wouldn't rate it quite that high.

Sammy put a slice of bread in the toaster. "Roy made a piece of toast not two minutes ago," I said, "why couldn't you have made yours then?"

"I was eating my cereal then," he said. "You told me to."

"From now on you don't use the toaster for one slice of toast. You don't start the dishwasher if it's only half full. You don't use the dryer for one sock. Now for baths—"

"We'll use the shower," Maggie said. "That way we can take them all at once."

Kit slammed down her spoon with a look of outrage. "I would sooner die," she stated.

"Save on soap too," Maggie said. "Lather up one of the kids and pass him around."

Kit jumped up from the table. "I don't believe you're my real mother!" She stalked out of the room.

Roy watched her go. "What's her trouble?"

Sammy was spreading jam on his toast. "She's mad," he said, "she sat on some chewing gum."

According to the book, saving electricity was supposed to bring the family closer together.

A little later I went back to the garage to check the meter. There were a bunch of little dials like clocks and one horizontal disk that kept turning all the time. It seemed to me that it was always going the same speed no matter how I tried to cut down on power. It didn't seem right. It was almost as though the meter was a dummy, put there to keep the customers happy. All the company did was figure out how much money it needed each month and send out bills accordingly. There was one way to find out. I went in the kitchen and turned on everything on the stove.

That really started it moving. Watching the wheel spin, it occurred to me that it had to take some power to run the meter itself and that power was rung up on the meter and on my bill. For every kilowatt hour it measured it used up a little extra and of course it measured that extra too. It was like interest compounded every second. Somebody, I decided, was going to get a mighty hot letter. I wasn't sure who, but somebody. I'd heard Maggie drive in a couple of minutes before. I went in to tell her.

The kitchen was smoky and Maggie appeared a little out of sorts. She was standing in a pool of milk and there were groceries all around the floor. She looked at me thoughtfully. "The phone was ringing when I came in," she said, "and I set the bag of groceries on the corner of the stove. When I got back the bag was on fire and everything in it had gone on the floor." She moved her foot, sending a little wave of milk across the linoleum. "Mind telling me why you had all the burners on high?"

When in doubt, they say, tell the truth. "I wanted to see if it would make the meter go faster."

"No." She shook her head. "Nobody would do that." She thought for a minute. "On the other hand, you might."

I started to help clean up. Canned goods, butter, three dozen eggs, a basket of mushrooms. "Were you planning something special for dinner?" I asked.

"Yes," she said. "I thought we'd have wall-to-wall omelet."

I think part of a parent's job is to teach his children to be saving. But somehow I always wind up the villain. Like the time last January when Roy caught cold. He told everybody it was because I made him take a shower with cold water. Actually there was a full tank of hot water, but he used it up to warm the bathroom while he was getting undressed. If his shower was a little cool it was entirely his own fault, but do you suppose I could sell that to his grandmother, or his teacher, or the neighbors? Or Mrs. Gulick at the confectionery? I think Eugene over at the car wash believed me, but what's one out of fourteen?

The same with the electric blankets. I discovered the boys were turning them on right after school so they'd be good and warm by bedtime. I had to keep going up and turning them off. As I was telling Mac down at the drugstore, you can't win. I had stopped in to get an elastic brace for a wrenched knee.

"How did it happen this time?" he asked.

I explained I was in the boys' room and stepped on a dumbbell in the dark. "I hadn't bothered to turn on a light," I said, "I just stepped in to turn off their electric blankets." As I turned my head I saw these two elderly women. They were staring at me with a certain lack of cordiality.

"Did you hear that?" one of them asked. "It was fifteen above last night."

"Roy get over his cold all right?" Mac asked. He is probably the biggest-mouthed pharmacist I've ever run into.

"Yes, sure," I said with a little laugh. "Just the sniffles. You know how kids are—never want to put on their warm sweaters, their nice warm jackets." I gave another laugh. I hate it when old ladies glare at me. I could feel two pairs of eyes on me like laser beams.

"Twisted his knee, did he?" one said. She made no effort to keep her voice down.

"Too bad it wasn't his neck," said the other.

"Having a special on cocktail mix," Mac said, "be a good time to stock up."

"No, no," I said, "no. A few things for the kiddies maybe—some vitamins—a sack of toys—"

Maggie picked up the sack I had put on the table. "Cod-liver oil and yo-yos," she said. "Where's the daiquiri mix?"

"Look," I told her, "if you don't like the way I shop, you do it."

"I wasn't complaining," she said. "I think you shop great."

One way to save power is to keep the refrigerator and freezing compartment full—less cold air to spill out when you open the door. Our refrigerator was pretty full but the freezer was half empty. I took a bunch of pint freezer containers, filled them with water and tucked them in all the empty spaces.

It was a couple of weeks later that I got a call from Mrs. Detweiler—they were new neighbors we hadn't met. She said Roy was playing with their boy and he said maybe we could spare some ice cubes. I said sure, send the boys over. Then I discovered our ice trays were practically empty so I took the ice out of a dozen or so containers and sent that over. I told the boy to tell his mother I was sorry we were almost out of ice cubes too.

When Roy came back he said Mrs. Detweiler told him to be sure and say thanks. Maggie said thanks for what?

"For the ice cubes," he told her. "She said she'd sure like to get a look at our drinking glasses."

As the book said, the heating system is the place where most energy is wasted. One evening when I had the house to myself I decided to try some of the tips I had never gotten around to. I poured myself a snifter of brandy and set the thermostat at sixty-six to make it a real challenge—I had an album of African folk music and I put that on for the psychological effect.

The first tip was to raise the humidity. I had tried setting pans of water around the house, but nobody remembered to keep them filled. Then I thought of Sammy's old wading pool. I dug it out, blew it up, and found it was still usable. I put it in the corner of the living room and filled it with a bucket. It took me eleven trips, but it seemed to me the room was more comfortable already.

Everybody feels the cold in different ways—with me it's ankles and the back of my neck. I hunted up a pair of fleece-lined boots and in the process I found a sort of Batman hood Maggie had made for one of the kids from an old satin wrap—it was just the ticket. I set the thermostat to sixty-four and turned over the record.

I picked up the book. Many houses have phantom drafts, it said, cold air coming from some unknown source. The way to track them down is to light a cigarette and follow the smoke back-ward. I wasn't smoking at the time, but I found some incense and lit that. Sure enough the smoke showed a definite draft. It seemed to be coming from in back of the pool down near the floor. I got down on my knees and waved the incense slowly back and forth over the water.

"I'm home," Maggie called from the hall. "I brought the Det-weilers along—they've been dying to meet you."

In summer it's the air conditioner that really sends up the elec-tric bill. One way around this, according to the book, is to use a fan in the attic to blow out the hot air. We happened to have a big one that just fit in the window. There was no outlet up there, so I ran an extension cord down to the hall and plugged it in.

"We'll give it a couple of hours," I told Maggie, "and see what difference it makes." It made quite a bit actually. In two hours the temperature was up eight degrees.

"You know that's a two-way fan," Maggie said, "are you sure you set it for exhaust?"

"What do you take me for," I asked, "some kind of dummy?" I looked around. "Maggie?" She wasn't there. I found her in the attic. "Well?" I said.

"You were right," she said, "it was set for exhaust. Only you put it in the window backward. Instead of exhausting the attic it was exhausting the world." She flipped the switch the other way. "For the last two hours it's been sucking up the bugs and dust and hot air from outside and pumping it all down the stairs."

Even with the fan reversed, it didn't seem to help. Kit said she couldn't see what the fan was supposed to do anyhow. "I should think that was pretty obvious," I said, "it blows out the hot air and brings up cool air from downstairs."

Roy said what was so good about that? "Listen," I said, "do you think you know more than the book?"

"Well," Sammy said, "the attic is where you keep stuff you don't need, so in the summertime it seems like a good place to keep hot air."

That night it rained in the attic window, loosening a big chunk of plaster in the hall. Looking back and considering the entire spectrum of the energy problem, I would have to say the attic fan is not one of your better answers.

One way to teach people to appreciate electricity is to see how they get along without it. One evening when the family was occupied with its various concerns, I threw the master switch. You'd have thought lightning had struck. Everybody was yelling at once to tell me the lights were out—the boys from the living room, Maggie from the kitchen, Kit from upstairs. It was the first time I could remember that the whole family had agreed on anything.

"Relax," I said, laughing, "this is only a test."

Maggie said to stop the clowning, she had an angel-food cake in the oven. Kit was painting her vanity, she said, hurry up with the lights. The boys said yes, they wanted their Eskimo Pies. I said it was no time to bother me with such trifles.

I felt my way back to the basement and threw the switch back on. The lights flashed and went off again. Maggie yelled down to please stop playing games.

"I turned it on," I yelled back. "Something else must be wrong. Where's the flashlight?"

She said Kit had it. Kit said she had a dripping paintbrush and no place to put it down. I told her to hold it straight up. She said she had and the paint was already up to her elbow.

I don't know why Kit and her mother both insist on dipping a brush all the way to the handle. If I've told them once—Maggie yelled to ask what I planned to do. I told her to try to find some matches.

"If you think I'm going to bake this angel-food cake with matches—"

"I'm going to phone Mac," I said, "he'll know what to do." I started shuffling toward the phone. Roy asked again about the Eskimo Pies. I told him please forget the Eskimo Pies. He said he already had. I asked what that was supposed to mean. He said he'd brought them in from the kitchen just as the lights went out and he couldn't remember where he'd put them. Kit yelled to hurry up, the paint was dripping off her elbow. I told her to change hands. I don't know why the younger generation can't seem to think for itself. Always has to be told everything. In my day— Maggie spoke quite sharply from the kitchen. I dialed the operator and gave her the number to call. She said I could dial the number direct.

I told her I knew that, but I had a little problem—I couldn't see the dial. There was a long pause, followed by a sniff and another pause. What would Florence Nightingale have done? I asked her. She sniffed again, but she rang the number.

Mac answered. I told him our electricity was off. He asked how long since I'd paid the bill. "It's not that," I said, "I threw the main switch."

He said that was my answer right there. "What else have you been doing these days?"

"Look," I told him, "I put the switch on and the lights flashed on and then off again." He asked what we had turned on at the time. The TV, I said, three air conditioners, the oven, refrigerator, washer, dryer, road racing set, lights, clocks, radios.

"Right," he said, "you see everything blasted on at the same time and blew your fuses. Matter of fact, it dimmed the street lights all over town."

I asked what he thought I should do. He asked if I believed in the power of prayer. "This is no time for jokes," I said, "I've got fallen angel food, missing Eskimo Pies, and a half-done vanity."

Mac said his advice to me was to take up a hobby. "Night sky diving might be just the ticket," he said.

I asked what the devil he was talking about.

"For the sake of your health," he said, "these quiet evenings at home are going to kill you."

Never Forget Jofs and Toks

When Maggie's nephew, Warren, decided to get married, she got him a book that was supposed to prepare him for family life. I couldn't help smiling. She wanted to know what was so funny. Actually, I said, it was more sad than funny.

It's like giving somebody a diploma in aeronautical engineering and all of a sudden he thinks he can fly. A fellow reads a book on family guidance and he's ready to take over a household. I know now why people cry at weddings—it's that happy smile on the face of the groom. You can just see him walking up to the cliff and jumping off, flapping his wings.

I know these books mean well, but, good Lord—they worry about the problem of families that find themselves broke by the end of the month. To me this is no problem, it's a goal.

Maggie said all right, if I knew so much why didn't I write a book? Okay, I said, only I don't need a whole book—a couple of pages will do.

For one thing, Warren, I'm not going to bother you with a lot of fancy laws. As any lawyer will tell you, it isn't the laws, it's the loopholes.

For example the law says that the pupils in Mrs. Nerlinger's second grade have to bring in thirty-four empty milk cartons by Tuesday. The loophole is, if you don't supply the cartons somebody else will. However, once you get married you find you have just become this somebody else. What looked like a loophole is really a pitfall. How do you tell the difference? Simple. When you're married, they're all pitfalls.

Now, you may say, this doesn't make sense. Right, and the sooner you learn to live with this the happier you'll be.

The books picture family life the way it used to be on those old magazine covers—freckle-faced kids, Dad with the pipe, Mom baking pies. Actually it's a lot more like Dali and the soft watches. In fact, to most family men the world of Dali is pretty ordinary.

So, Warren, why not join me in a stroll down Memory Lane? Or at least as far as the garage.

One fact you have to accept is that kids get some strange notions. For instance, Sammy thought that shoes would grow if you kept wearing them. I asked where he got that idea, and he said from me. Well, he had these perfectly good shoes that he refused to wear and all I said was if he didn't wear them they'd get too small. The point is that buying kids shoes is more emotional than logical.

Like the time the manager down at the Drug Mart got so upset because Roy and Sammy were lying in front of his store with their bare feet against the window. As I pointed out, he was the one who decided to have the sneaker sale and presumably also the one who put up the sign saying nobody allowed inside with bare feet. Hence my dilemma.

I couldn't take the kids in to the shoes unless they were wearing shoes. I couldn't take the shoes out to the kids until I knew what size they needed, which I was attempting to ascertain through the glass when the man had his attack.

What did he expect? I asked, when the inferior sneakers he carried wouldn't last from one sale to the next? I suggested he hold his sales every week—either that or sell his sneakers in six-packs. He didn't answer.

I asked Maggie how her guidance book would handle a situation like this. She didn't answer either. The point is, Warren, nothing is ever as simple as it looks. Just because the top is on the ketchup bottle that doesn't mean it's fastened on.

This one time Maggie was making sandwiches in the kitchen and I was carving cold roast pork when she asked me for the ketchup. I picked it up by the top. I happened to be in the middle of one of my James Cagney impressions and as I was talking, the top came off and the bottle dropped five and a half feet. The kitchen floor came up and smacked the bottle like a giant hand and the ketchup spurted all the way to my shoulder and down my shirt and pants. I had just come to the part where I was saying, "Nobody double-crosses me," and I sort of mumbled the rest—"you dirty rat."

Maggie stood looking at me and then her face started breaking up. She dropped the butter knife and when she stooped to pick it up she collapsed in a heap.

While I was standing there, trying to think of something to say, Edna Hoffmier from across the street came in the back door. Her eyes moved from Maggie on the floor to the knife in my hand and my shirt. She said, "Oh dear," in a high, thin voice and passed out. Just how much coverage, I wonder, does the book give to situations of this nature?

As you see, Warren, small things can make all the difference—like the flashlight battery tester. This is a little wire frame that you hold against the battery to see if it will light up a flashlight bulb.

You will note I said flash*light* bulb—not *flash*bulb. There is a world of difference. Nothing looks more harmless than a flashlight battery, but this is only if you have never tested one with a flashbulb. Talk about fast. A flashbulb will go from room temperature to seven hundred degrees in less time than it takes to let go of it.

Maggie wanted to know what had happened to my hand. "Pick up the soldering iron by the wrong end again?" Forget it, I said.

Maybe a few rules would be in order:

1. Don't keep oven cleaner in the oven.
2. When the kitchen sink is stopped up, you'll have to take off the S-shaped piece of pipe, so put a pan underneath to catch the water.
3. Do this first.
4. Don't empty the pan into the sink until you have put back the S-shaped piece.
5. Don't forget Jofs and Toks. I'm afraid I can't tell you what this means at the moment, but it's written down in my notes—it's even underlined so it's obviously important and no doubt will become clear in due time.

A word about lead pencils. We have three pencil sharpeners but at least half our pencils have been hand-sharpened. This is done by breaking off pieces of wood with the thumbnail. And all the erasers are gone. New pencils that haven't written six words have erasers worn down to the metal. Don't ask me why. Anybody with kids knows they never correct anything. But there they are. I could probably show you forty pencils, Warren, the points blunt and splintered, the erasers gone, but don't ask me why. When you become a family man, past experience goes for naught. Logic is no longer your friend.

Like a few weeks ago, when Maggie asked me who A. Chang was. She was sitting on the living-room floor trying to straighten a bicycle fender.

"Chang?" I said, "A. Chang?" It sounded like a trick question. "Is he somebody we know?"

"I didn't say it was a he," she said. "It could be Amy Chang, could be Agnes Chang."

"Could be Annie Laurie Chang," Roy said.

"Annette Funicello Chang," Sammy said.

"All right," I said. "It could be Alice Blue Gown Chang, but I fail to see that this is getting us anywhere." I turned to Maggie. "Is this some Chinese person we know?"

Maggie put down her hammer. "If I knew who it was, would I ask you?"

Sammy said his teacher did. "She says stuff like who was Johnny Appleseed and she already knows."

93

Roy said everybody knew about J. Appleseed but what about A. Chang?

Maggie held the fender up to the light. "He seems to be some Chinese friend that Dad wants to invite to dinner."

"Oh," I said, "you mean *that* A. Chang." If she wanted to play games, okay. "Yes, he came along later," I said, "traveled all over the Middle West." Doing what? Sammy asked.

I picked up my newspaper. "Chopping down apple trees," I said. Sammy wanted to know how come. I didn't know how come. Roy did. For the birds' nests, he said, use them for soup.

"Yes," Maggie said, "I remember now. He had a jinricksha and traded with the Indians." Roy wanted to know what he traded. "Tea and firecrackers," she said. "And he did their washing."

Sammy looked at me. "He's coming here for dinner?"

"Ask your mother," I told him, "she started it."

"You wrote it down," Maggie said, "right here on this shopping list: 'How about some Chinese food for A Chang?'"

"Let me have my glasses." I put them on. "How about some Chinese food—that's 'for a change,'" I said, "can't you read English?"

"I could if anybody would write it," she said.

"You mean there isn't any A. Chang?" Roy asked.

Sammy said, "And he's not coming to supper?"

"No," I said, "he was sort of a mistake. A misprint."

"Well, heck," Sammy said, "I was counting on him." He was staring at the floor, the picture of dejection. "I thought we could go for a ride in the ricksha and shoot off the firecrackers in the vacant lot." You could tell he had been seeing himself as the hero of the neighborhood and now it was only words. He was holding his mouth tight.

Maggie moved over beside him and smoothed back his hair. "Listen, Charlie Chan," she said, "has Dad ever let you down?"

"I guess not." He gave her a wavering smile.

So there it is. I'm going to have to come up with something. What, I don't know. But something. Meanwhile I keep seeing that little oriental fellow. He's pulling his ricksha through the forest glades, trading the Indians lichee nuts and helping them build a wall around Ohio.

I just figured out about Jofs and Toks. The first one stands for *The Joy of Sex,* which I was to pick up at the library. Toks are Tik Toks, a clock-shaped cheese cracker Maggie wanted to try. I remember she was mad because I sat up half the night reading Jofs and the bed got full of Toks crumbs.

I guess that sums it up, Warren, a little give, a little take, sometimes better, sometimes worse—just keep smiling and play your cards the way they fall—Jofs today, tomorrow Toks, and that's what married life is all about.

Gift Horse

When it comes to giving your wife a present, there's no place for calm reasoning—you must follow the dictates of your heart. Literature is full of examples—the free spirit who gives his beloved a cherry that has no stone, a glass slipper, a partridge in a pear tree. The trouble is, following the dictates of your heart is not the easiest thing in the world. Figuring birthdays, anniversaries, Mother's Day and Christmas, that's four times a year you're supposed to go out and be whimsical and spontaneous, and your average husband just isn't up to it.

Usually I go to a gift shop first, against my better judgment. These places are jam-packed with things you can't make head or tail of. It's not so bad in the summertime, but when you're wearing an overcoat you're lucky to get out without doing three or four dollars' worth of damage. For ordinary browsing, I'll take a hardware store every time.

Or a department store. The lady behind the counter always

tries to be helpful. She asks things like what size and what color and does she like tailored or frilly clothes?

Okay—Maggie's favorite color is green but it makes her complexion look muddy, she says, so forget that. At the moment she's a sixteen on a diet and aiming for twelve so don't get her anything real nice in a sixteen. However she's been sixteen going on twelve for as long as I can remember, so we won't worry about that. She does like frilly things. She got herself a blouse all covered with ruffles and flounces and she loved it until a friend asked her what did she hear from Scarlett and Rhett? and she hasn't worn it since.

One salesgirl asked if Maggie was an indoor or outdoor person. I had to stop and think. I could picture her in the yard hanging up the wash or carrying out the garbage, but that was before we got the dryer and the disposal unit. Part indoor, part out, I guess you'd say. The girl said what did she like?

For one thing she liked to put on an old flannel robe in the evening with some Alan Jones records in the background, and do jigsaw puzzles and eat peanut brittle. She'd sit there with a piece of the puzzle in one hand, a piece of candy in the other. As she fit the pieces of puzzle into place, she'd snap off a piece of brittle with her teeth. And in the background, "The Donkey Serenade." It was a warm, homey picture, but for gift suggestions a washout.

Of course the traditional presents for a wife are flowers, candy, and perfume, and I expect most women would be glad to receive any of these if only they weren't quite so traditional. These are things a man can buy without even leaving the office, over the phone. In fact, it's forgetful husbands who keep the five-pound box of chocolates manufacturers in business. However, there may be times when you're absolutely stuck, can't think of anything else, in which case your best bet is to be audacious—buy all three —flowers, candy, and perfume. I've never done this myself, but if someone else would like to try, I'd certainly be happy to know how it turns out.

Taking the kids to buy their mother a present can be pretty harrowing. They love to do it—they want to buy her everything in sight as long as it's gaudy. I try to steer them toward the little flowered cream pitcher and away from the Balinese dancing girls. No use. Their idea of the perfect Mother's Day gift is something with plenty of red satin and jewels and a powerful smell of jasmine. I don't know where we get the idea of the American Mom as an apple-cheeked little lady rolling pie crust. My experience is that most boys think Mom ought to look like a friend of Toulouse-Lautrec.

There's an old axiom that you should never buy your wife anything she would buy for herself, but it seems to me this is an axiom that cuts both ways. Does she never buy it because it's too expensive? Or because she wouldn't be caught dead with it? My own selections more often than not seem to fall in the latter category.

I used to try to get Maggie to say just what she wanted. She said that would take all the fun out of it.

"Okay," I said, "but where are all those fun presents I've given you before? The bulldog doorstop—the Chinese birdfeeder? Up in the attic."

So finally she said she'd like a clock. I wrote down all the details to be sure to get it right.

She opened the other presents first—the buttonhole attachment for her sewing machine from her mother, put on the tiara from Roy, and sprayed the atomizer from Sammy. Then she unwrapped my present, rolling up the ribbon and folding the paper. "A clock," she said, "just what I've always wanted."

"Early American coachman," I said, "polystyrene-simulated Black Forest carved walnut case."

"I can see," she said.

"Antiqued gold foil dial," I went on, reading from my notes, "with swinging pendulum—twelve and a half inches by twenty-two."

"It *is* big," she said. "I hadn't realized."

"Swinging pendulum," I said, "simulated weights, gold color plastic bezel. Everything just what you asked for."

"I know," she said, "just what I asked for." The next day she exchanged it for a wok.

A woman has it easy when it comes to buying her husband a

present. She can make something and he can't. She can bake him a cake, prepare his favorite dinner, and knit him a sweater, and everybody will say how sweet, a gift from the heart. But let him fix her favorite dinner and make her a fern stand and people will simply call him cheap.

Women who write advice columns are very partial to the offbeat present. I think that if you're dealing with mink or platinum you can be offbeat as all get out and never worry. On the other hand—well, Maggie loves to grow flowers, and our soil is pretty poor. So I happened to meet this fellow who had a riding academy. I already knew a fellow with a truck. This was right after I'd read the offbeat column.

The problem is, a female gardener is a female first and she wants to make a good impression on other females. When she stretches out her hand to show what hubby has given her she'd like to be showing off a ring or a watch and not pointing to something behind the garage.

Not that she complained—the only reference I heard was a remark to her sister over the phone. "I know about gift horses," she said, "a gift horse I wouldn't mind."

People say, well, if you can't decide what to give her, why not a gift certificate? As far as I can see this is the same as a check, except you can only cash it one place. And giving your wife a check when you have a joint account must be the bull's-eye of futility.

Our last anniversary I was going to give Maggie a new robe, but she said she didn't want to give up her old one. "I'll tell you what I *would* like, though—a housecoat. Something as warm as my robe but a little more dressy. Something I can wear to fix breakfast if we have company." I said fine.

I got home late and the kids were in bed. I handed Maggie the box. "Happy Anniversary."

"Certainly feels light," she opened it, "what in the world? A peignoir set." She held it up. "Good heavens, you could read fine print through it."

I said I knew. "The girl at the store held it up for me to look through. I could see a bus going by outside."

"This is what she recommended for someone fixing breakfast for company?"

I'd forgotten about that. "You think it might be a little distracting?"

"Well," she said, "if you don't mind cornflakes in your hair and syrup in your shoes."

"She did show me a housecoat," I said, "it looked sort of—I don't know—like Whistler's Mother. I couldn't get that for you— not on our anniversary."

"Not on our anniversary," she said softly, "so how did she happen to show you this?"

I cleared my throat. "I said it was for my secretary."

She seemed to be having trouble with her throat too. She put the present in the box and went upstairs. When I went in the bedroom she was modeling it in front of the mirror. "Well," I said, "well, well."

"Yes," she said, "I feel like a friend of Toulouse-Lautrec."

I sat down on the bed and started taking off my shoes. "You think it will keep you warm?"

She drew herself up in front of the mirror. A fine figure of a woman, Maggie. "Well"—she made a little pirouette—"it may need a little help."

"You can count on it," I told her.

Only a Game

I'd seen game shows before, but I never realized what a cinch they were until the week I was home with the flu.

"It's pathetic," I remarked to Maggie, "here's this college kid from Oxnard who doesn't know who wrote Hiawatha, can't name one ingredient in pancakes, and he walks off with eighteen hundred dollars and a Pontiac."

"I don't know why you don't get on one of those shows," she replied. "We could sure use a new car."

Well, I thought, why not? "Not that I'm prejudiced," I said, "but if a twenty-two-year-old from Southern California can win, anybody can win."

I spent the whole week studying game shows. It was a whole new world—or at least a whole new neighborhood and a very chummy, close-knit one.

In theory these are amateur shows and the stars are the contestants, but after one appearance they're through, so it is the MCs and celebrities who are the bread-and-butter players. Some MCs have more than one show and they often appear as guest MCs or celebrities on other shows. Some celebrities seem to be much in demand and you can see them on two or three shows a day. In fact, there are some you never see any place else. This is the only thing they are celebrated for. Being celebrities.

Game-show audiences are mostly gray-haired and good-natured. They don't have to pay to get in, the seats are comfortable, and they're all set to laugh and clap. It doesn't take much to set them off. Mention Scarsdale—those who have heard of it will laugh, those who haven't will clap.

The contestants are mostly young and good-looking, and they kiss like there was no tomorrow. Girls who win kiss the MC. He kisses all the good-looking girls, winners, losers, girls who are there by mistake. The celebrities kiss each other.

What the studio audience does is hard to say because you don't see them much. But I suppose they fool around some. What the heck? I know they clap a lot. Everybody does.

When I was young, you didn't clap for yourself. That was as bad as voting for yourself for class president. If you did something good you were supposed to scuff your foot and mumble. Not any more.

When a fellow wins he claps with his hands over his head like a boxer. A girl claps real fast with her hands in front of her face and her elbows held in. When she wins big she presses her hands against the sides of her head, like squeezing a sponge. And squeals. She also jumps up and down. That's the part I like best.

Now it may not be modest to clap when you win, but at least it's understandable. These people even clap when they don't win. On one show, before you find out what your prize is going to be they show you what's behind the curtain you didn't pick and they all stand there clapping like crazy for all the stuff they're not getting—patio furniture, mink stole, motorboat. It's all going back to the warehouse, so what? It gets a standing ovation. You can't help feeling these people would applaud a flu epidemic.

I hadn't been watching long before I realized that game shows had come a long way since the days of "The Quiz Kids" and little

Joel Kupperman. My Lord, I hadn't thought of his name in years. I went back to tell Maggie. She was standing on a chair, vacuuming the closet shelves. She shook her head, pointing to the vacuum. As she started to get down the chair tilted and she banged her knee against the door. She hobbled over to turn off the machine. "What did you say?" she asked.

I said, "I was just saying I hadn't thought of the name Joel Kupperman in thirty years."

She stood there looking at me for about a minute, rubbing her knee. Maybe a minute and a half. Then she turned on the vacuum and climbed back on the chair.

All right, I still think it's remarkable the way the mind can come up with a name after thirty years. Thirty-five would be more like it.

Of course it's the MC who's the backbone of the show, and his job isn't as easy as it looks. He has to deal with the ignorant, the mercenary, and the inane and make it all somehow seem like television's finest hour.

On one show where men were competing with women, the MC picked out a team of Lorraine, Debbie, and Joanne. "This is the ladies' team," he said. Then, feeling this might be a little obvious, he added, "Obviously." A little later he said, "Well, why don't we start with the first round?" Your top-notch MC can take remarks like these and make them sound pretty profound. The sort of fellow you expect to find as speaker at the Little League banquet.

Between inflation and competition there is a skyrocketing of prize money and the problem is for a show to keep from going broke without looking cheap. This is where a good MC earns his keep. The fellow who can say SEH VUN TEEN HUN DRED DOLL ERZ and make it sound like SEH VUN TEEN THOW ZUND DOLL ERZ can write his own ticket.

Often the MC has an assistant—a kind of Sancho Panza. He's usually sort of dumb and funny and does little skits and carries packages—like an uncle at a birthday party. Another of his jobs is describing all the prizes in about a minute without slighting any of them. This can be a problem, because he may have to make two dozen cans of Mexican dinner sound as exciting as a week's vacation in Honolulu. The Mexican dinners may not seem like much, as prizes go, but the company that puts them out may be fifteen or twenty times as big as the company that puts out the Hawaiian vacation and is very important to the people who are putting out the game show. This is why the assistant MC has to lean so hard on the enchiladas and the refried beans.

The celebrities spend their time telling each other what night clubs or theaters they are appearing in that week. And congratulating each other on their new show. And kissing. At first I was worried about the celebrities appearing in public without their writers—afraid they would make dumb mistakes and embarrass themselves. I shouldn't have worried. They made the dumb mistakes all right, but it didn't embarrass them. I suspect there are things that do embarrass celebrities, but general run-of-the-mill ignorance isn't one of them.

The average person, finding himself enmeshed in a pointless anecdote will drop it as soon as he can. The celebrity will embroider it. To him it is a mark of distinction—like having his trash bronzed.

"It took me six months to get my wife to cook eggplant for my lunch," he says, "and that night we went out to dinner—and this you won't believe—we had eggplant again." Then, surveying his stunned audience, he raises his right hand. "I swear," he says, "this really happened."

The MC goes about it a little differently. "You're from Springfield?" he says to the contestant. "I have a cousin that used to live in Springfield—he ran the theater there. What's the name of it? The Springfield Theater, that's right. My cousin used to run it."

All the MC is trying to do is show the people that he knows something besides what's written down on those cards. When he gets a chance he makes the most of it. That's why he likes to talk about what kind of dog he has and his favorite flavor of ice cream.

He doesn't always know the contestant's home town but he's pretty sure there's a lot of beautiful country around there. That's right the contestant says, there sure is. Mud Flat New Jersey, Strip Mine, West Virginia, no matter.

One thing that bothered me was that 70 per cent of the contestants came from Southern California. Never any from Vermont. Maggie thought it was probably the weather. "They have such great air in Vermont. Not to mention the maple syrup. Who needs L.A.?"

"There aren't any contestants from Delaware either," I said, "and they don't have such great air. Maple syrup either."

"That's always bothered me," she said.

Any contestant that's married always has a wonderful wife or husband and fabulous kids. The divorce rate is soaring, kids are dropping out of school and taking to the streets, but contestants all have an ecstatic home life.

"Where do they get all these wonderful contestants?" I asked Maggie.

"Are they all like that?" she asked.

"Every one," I said, "they're as sweet and interchangeable as marshmallows. Try naming all the wonderful people we know." She didn't answer. "Were you listening?"

"I'm thinking," she said. "There's the Hennessys."

I stared. "Are you out of your mind? You said yourself their kids are monsters. Eileen spends all her afternoons playing bridge. Clint got in a fight with a bartender just last week."

"You said wonderful," she said, "you didn't say fabulous."

One thing that surprised me was the amount of sex in the game shows. They had questions like: Can a woman find as much satisfaction in work as in romance? And by romance they didn't mean Nelson Eddy singing to Jeanette MacDonald. It was something much closer to home.

And the celebrities would drag in some joke with a double meaning whenever they could which was most of the time. Actually they weren't very funny. They weren't even very dirty. Dingy would be a better word—like something washed in Brand X.

There was a show where everybody dressed up in crazy costumes in hopes of being called on. Only a dozen could make it, which left three hundred or so all dressed up and no place to go but home. You would picture them waiting there at the bus stop, the scarecrow, the walking banana, the fellow with the tomahawk in his skull and 297 more, all looking glum and getting pointed out to sightseeing buses.

There was one girl dressed up like a woolly-bear caterpillar. She was a fat girl and she had traded back and forth until she had a basket of cheese and an envelope of money. She could have traded for what was behind the curtain, but decided to keep what she had. So they showed what was behind the curtain—luggage, wristwatch, vacation in Rio and much more. When she opened the envelope there was five dollars inside. So she had that and the cheese.

The MC rose to the occasion, saying you can't win them all. She looked at him for a moment, blinking. And then she smiled.

To me all the winners were pretty much indistinguishable, with the hands against the head and the shrieking and the jumping. But the fat girl with her woolly-bear suit and her basket of cheese —she was special. I hoped if I were ever in a spot like that I would show as much class.

It seems to me the game shows have covered it all—from "How's Your Spouse?" to "Name That Isthmus." They even have one where they give the answer and you have to supply the question.

Moosejaw, Canada.

Where was Art Linkletter born?

I have decided they're not for me—I would lose either way. If I blew the big prize and said Bert Parks instead of Art Linkletter, it would haunt me the rest of my life. And I can't think of anything I would hate more to be haunted by.

Even if I won—how could I enjoy my stay at the Pompei Hilton if I kept seeing the girl with her woolly-bear suit and her forgiving smile?

The morning I went back to work, Maggie asked if I'd gotten anything out of my week at home. The answer was easy.

Game shows.

What do I don't care if I never see another of?

106

Down the White Water

Anybody'd told me a year ago that I'd be taking three boys on a white water raft trip, I'd have said one of us was crazy. I'd have been right. Turned out to be me.

Trip was sponsored by the Y, and the kids couldn't go without me. Sorry, I said, not my bag of tea. No tea, they said, just bag. My kids will argue about anything. Besides, they said, Sonny Rundy's father was going.

My wife said Sonny Rundy's father was about thirty-five years old. Asked her what that had to do with it. Everything, she said. Rafting was a sport for younger men. Oh? I said. Really? Really, she said. Reminded me I had caught cold the last time I washed the car. So what? Sonny Rundy, Sr., was the type who carried a compass to the drugstore. Chinned himself at parties.

Twenty people on the bus—Rundy, me, Harry the driver, Miss Benbow from the Y, four girls and twelve boys. Passing through Frederick and Hagerstown, country rich in scenery and tradition.

Inside the bus air heavy with the sound of disc jockey and the scent of artificial grape gum. Even in the wilderness, part of home would be with us.

Some people find teen-agers obnoxious. Should try three hundred miles of them in bus. Humor. "Oh, is that a cow? I thought it was Ricky's girl." Three Minutes Uninterrupted Laughter. "No, Ricky's girl isn't that good-looking." T. More M. U. L.

Between jokes, singing. Thirty-eight verses of "There Was an Old Lady Who Swallowed a Fly." Sonny Rundy, Sr., conducting.

Often wondered why such nice little boys turn into such impossible teen-agers. Think I know. The realization that a man will never be young again is a pretty sobering thing. But the looks and words and acts of the teen-ager make growing old a lot easier to take.

Camp site on wooded hillside overlooking lake—six or eight cabins and dining shed with picnic tables and fireplace. No doubt more than adequate by camping standards. To someone whose idea of roughing it was non-automatic ice-maker and black and white TV, it was a little stark. Everybody running around, blowing whistles, yelling orders and trying to outwoodcraft everybody else. Couldn't figure out what to do with my suitcase. Sonny Rundy's father suggested I stow it in my Appalachian. About to give him sharp retort when I discovered it was name for log cabin with one wall missing. Appalachian they call it. Big deal.

Figured out where to put my cot and sleeping bag, but where do you put your pills and the water to take them with? Sat there on cot remembering my first day in Army. My name was down to clean latrine and I didn't know what it was.

Feeling better by suppertime. Chance to observe kids eating, putting away trapper's soup and chicken. Discovered one cause of food shortage—nobody today knows how to eat fried chicken. Bite and a half from a drumstick and throw it away. Remembered my boyhood. When we had chicken there weren't any scraps—our ants had to go next door to eat.

Kept feeling something missing. Finally figured it out. No cocktail hour. Not much of a drinker, but a couple martinis offer pleasant social interlude—relaxation—conversation break. On a bad day, give you something to shoot for—focal point. Trapper's soup doesn't do the same job.

Had quit smoking a week before. Good example for boys—see one adult who wasn't slave to nicotine. After supper sat around not smoking. Nobody noticed. Happened to mention I hadn't smoked in over a week. Sonny Rundy, Sr., unwrapped stick of gum. Said he'd never smoked. Told him I'd never chewed gum. Very interesting, he said. Harry and Miss Benbow setting up schedule for next day. Said I hadn't smoked in a week and didn't even miss it. Harry said he hadn't smoke in ten years and didn't miss it. Miss B said she hadn't smoked in twenty-eight years and didn't miss it. Not the same thing at all. Couldn't seem to get it through their heads. Little kid pumping water. Told him I hadn't smoked in a week and didn't miss it. Said he'd quit two years ago and didn't miss it.

Kids playing Beep Beep. If you say a word starting with B you have to say Beep Beep or everybody gets to sock you. Decided to join in. Point of game is do other things—cook marshmallows, sing, tell jokes. Did fine until one of the boys asked me to do my Crosby imitation. B B B Boo. Stupid game.

My boys on worst behavior, fighting, calling names. Ashamed of them, I said—think twice before taking them next time. They said if I'd thought twice I wouldn't have taken them this time.

Park cop came around. Asked how everything was. Told him fine. Hadn't smoked in over a week. He said fine.

Bed eleven o'clock. Couldn't sleep. Took two sleeping pills. No help. Remembered I'd forgotten to get sleeping pills. Took two of something. Wind blowing, leaves rustling, branches creaking. Something crawling on roof. Birds calling. Thought woods supposed to be so damned silent. Tried counting sheep. Got to 750. Sheep all drinking martinis and smoking cigarettes. Stopped counting.

Up five-thirty. Freezing. Started big fire. Make it nice for the rest. Good camper thinks of others. Others up seven-thirty just as firewood ran out. Said I'd get more. Wasn't any. Back in ten minutes with three pieces size of clothespins. Sonny Rundy, Sr., had big fire going—rolled-up newspapers. Old camper's trick he said. Rundy and others gazing at fire as if he'd invented it.

Bus to river. Four-man life rafts—twenty-five or thirty of them. Guides in special rafts and kayaks. Said in first rapid the current flows to left so keep to right of big rock shaped like whale. River full of big rocks. Ninety per cent looked like whales.

Current pushing us to left. Told kids to paddle harder. They were splashing each other and arguing. Told ones on right to backpaddle. Quit completely. Hit rock and spun around. Paddling like mad. By myself. Kids have paddles out of the water, poking each other and yelling. Guide in kayak pointing to where we were supposed to go. Suggested to him we trade places—let him paddle for a while and I'd take over the pointing. Didn't hear me. Saw Rundy and crew go by straight as an arrow. Like streetcar. If that's your idea of sport, okay. At the end of rapids, guide in kayak came over. Said it was first time a raft had shot the entire rapids backward. Told him I'd always been something of a pathfinder.

Guide gathered everybody together and explained next rapids. Said watch out for rock shaped like elephant. Hogwash. Tried that last time. Watched out for rock shaped like whale and hit rock shaped like tank. Guide looked my way. "Got that, Raft 66?" he asked. "Got it," I said.

Next rapid kids arguing again—got hung up on rock to the right. Kayak came over. Another first, he said. Nobody had ever hit that rock before. Didn't even know it was there.

Last boat through. Other boats gave us cheer. Decided next time we'd be first. Would have been if we hadn't hung up again. Guide called to buddy—Pathfinder's found another new one. Other boats shooting by—all paddling in unison like Mohawks. Me spinning around, going sideways with my little debating society.

Next rapid tried to fend off rock and leaned out too far. Guide on bank threw me rope. Scrambled up on rock to let next raft go by. Held up rope to clear their heads. Almost did. Fellow sore. Said have to be idiot to fall out of raft. Pointed out only one fell out of ours—all four fell out of his. Didn't answer.

Back in raft paddling down quiet stretch. Boys asked how I felt. Wet, I said, but good—cool. Boys looked at each other. Looked at me. You could see the wheels turning. Man overboard had kind of appeal. The next quarter mile all three fell overboard. Accidentally. Such acting I hadn't seen since silent movies.

I let them paddle and slumped down, enjoying the river. The Youghiogheny. Good name for it. Sounds like a river full of rocks. Some the size of bungalows. Some the size of laundromats. Thick woods climbing the hills on either side. Lovely spot if you like rocks and trees.

George Washington came up this river hunting for water route to Fort Pitt. Gave it up. Good eye for a river—George. Delaware, Potomac, Rappahannock. Youghiogheny was the only one he lost.

Stopped for lunch at big rock. Bread—sandwich makings all spread out. Long lines jostling, shoving. Decided not to stand in line. For pheasant maybe. Beneath my dignity to jostle for liverwurst. Saw Rundy eating triple-decker peanut butter and jelly. Asked how come no pemmican?

Rundy said peanut butter high in protein—jelly for quick energy. Very serious—anxious to convince me. Told him forget it. No need for Americans to explain peanut butter and jelly. Like apologizing for apple pie.

Rations nearly gone. Boys said better hurry—others going back for seconds and thirds. Little gluttons. Best I could manage was liverwurst sandwich. Had to do some jostling to get that.

Down river again. Had drink of river water—guide said okay. Tasted flat without the chlorine. Boys looked horrified. Told them try it—might be last chance.

Raft moving better—passing others—boys grinning like jack-o'-lanterns. Falling overboard good for esprit de corps. Dry raftsmen in other boats getting more tense with each rapid—like pitcher with no-hitter going. Best bet to fall out early and relax.

Hands blistered, sunburned, mosquito bites. Great trip. Enjoyed every minute. Told guide afterward—unique experience. He said guides felt same way.

Back to camp. Cot looked beautiful. Kids wanted to hike. Okay. Sonny Rundy's father our leader. Pointed out white pine, bird's-eye maple, sassafras. Rah rah rah. Said Indians made sas-safras tea. Kids wanted to make some. Okay with me. Came run-ning up later—handed me bundle of roots. About a half bushel. Told them enough. Sonny, Sr., very concerned. Illegal to take plants from state park. Better throw away roots before park cop saw me. Boys unhappy. Hesitated. Could see headlines—LOCAL MAN HELD: CHARGED UNLAWFUL POSSESSION OF SASSAFRAS.

Boys asked if I was going to throw it away. Said certainly not. Indians didn't believe in wasting sassafras. Neither did I. That evening the camp smelled like a sassafras growers' convention. After Rundy's carrying on, the boys seemed to have the idea that sassafras tea was somehow illegal. Worked like beavers chopping wood and building up the fire so ours would be darker, thicker, and more potent than the next Appalachian's. First time they worked together the whole trip. Took home canteen full—looked like molasses. Tasted like something Frankenstein might serve to Dracula. If not illegal it should have been.

My wife asked how the trip was. Said fine. Asked how boys behaved. Fine. How did I get along with Mr. Rundy? Fine. Raised her eyebrows.

Kids said I could camp rings around Mr. Rundy. "He took them down the rapids frontward. Dad took us down backward. He wanted to throw away the sassafras—he was afraid of the cops. But Dad wouldn't let him. Dad isn't scared of any cop there is." Told them to start unpacking.

Wife looking at me with peculiar expression. Told her kids hard to figure—Rundy practically Daniel Boone—Ph.D. in fron-tiersmanship and campology. Always did everything right.

Had to, she said, couldn't afford to make mistakes. Afraid to shatter Daniel Boone image. Kids rather be with me—make all the mistakes I wanted—no image to worry about.

Made sense. Not a whole lot, but still—

Kids don't want somebody perfect, she said, rather have some-body feeling his way same as they are.

Fair enough.

Pilgrims were lousy woodsmen, she said, not one out of ten

could start a fire. But they kept going, didn't quit, and that's what made the country what it is.

I nodded. Reached over and took swig of sassafras. "Just call me Pathfinder," I told her.

Goblins, Go Home

Ever notice the way Halloween has been going down hill? Used to be great time for kids. Tip things over. Throw stuff around. Good for you. Release aggression. Not any more. Kids put on sleazy costumes—collect midget candy bars—condemned bubble gum.

Damn shame. Kids gypped out of birthright. Decided to do something about it. Explained to Maggie. "Oh my God," she observed. Said kids in enough trouble without encouragement.

Told her not to take defeatist attitude. No trouble. Only harmless pranks. Hi jinks. Soap windows. Throw rotten tomatoes. Maggie said where do you find rotten tomatoes? Good point. Hardly ever see them any more. Told her we'd use fresh ones. She said at forty-nine cents a pound why not just throw money? Negative thinking.

Called in boys. Sammy and Roy. Asked how they'd like old-fashioned Halloween. Tip over garbage cans. Put pins in doorbells. Got blank looks. Can't understand kids today. No spirit. No

gumption. Squatted down. Took them by arm. "Don't you want
to have a little fun?" I asked. "What the devil is wrong with you?"
Maggie annoyed. Accused me of badgering kids. Dropped subject.
Didn't forget it.

Halloween I offered to take boys into town. Good place for
trick or treat. Houses close together. Sidewalks. Etc. Maggie suspi-
cious but willing. Boys eager. Sammy dressed as clown. Roy as pirate. Plastic pails. Identification tag on each costume. My name—
address—phone number. Good thinking.

Parked in middle of block. Let kids collect treats. Last house
man gave them jack-o'-lantern. Told them enough treats. Time
for tricks. Gave each one bar of soap. Told them sneak in and
draw on windows. Skull and crossbones—scarecrow—so forth.
Came back. Said they couldn't reach windows. Always excuses.

Moved on. Found good spot. Lots of shrubbery. Sneaked in.
Lifted Sammy up to window. Told him to get going. Said screen
in the way. Took a look. Sammy right. Hard to believe anybody
would leave screens up until October. Somebody ought to tell
them.

Left. Roy said don't forget pumpkin. I hadn't. Hoped he had.
Forty pounds and slippery. Also carrying Sammy's hat and Roy's
mask. Stopped at house. Gave boys pins. Told them to put in
doorbell. Back in minute. No doorbell. Next house same deal.
Looked around. No garbage cans. No tomatoes. Asked boys what
they'd like to do. Said go to bathroom. Told them wait until we
got home. No dice.

Problem of walking up to strange house—ask to use bathroom.
Why not? People understanding. Halloween especially. Started up
walk. Stopped. Couldn't do it. Can't explain. Woman could do it.
Man no. Can't get there from here.

Looked around. No gas stations. Neon light in distance. Emil's
Bar and Grill. Told boys follow me. Any port in storm. Pretty
ratty-looking port. Showed kids men's room. Put pails on bar. Also
hat, mask, pumpkin. Ordered drink. Hate to use men's room without buying something.

Solitary drinker couple of stools away. Hat pushed back. Necktie loose. Red face. Spoke to bartender—Emil. Pointed remark

about big kid not satisfied with one pail. Spoil it for all the others. Ignored him.

Emil brought drink. Asked which pail I wanted it in. Told him just serve the drink—never mind the comedy. Drunk moved over to next stool. Asked if I minded personal question. Shrugged. "How come you're wearing pirate mask with clown hat?" he asked. "What the hell you supposed to be?"

Pointed out I wasn't wearing the stuff. Didn't satisfy him. "Got two pails," he said, "two different costumes." Turned to blonde down the bar. "How you figure a kid like that?"

Blonde gave him fuzzy look. "Split personality."

Didn't know what was keeping boys. Finished drink. Ordered another. Sounded to me as though somebody outside was singing hymns. Women's voices. Emil looked at watch. Said, "starting early tonight." He could hear them too. Glad of that. Asked what it was all about. Emil explained. Group of church ladies trying to get saloon closed. Picketed place every evening. Sang hymns. Passed out tracts. Recalled reading about it in paper.

Boys came out of rest room. Ready to go. Told them no rush. Put them on stools. Ordered drinks. Ginger ale with cherry. Reviewed situation. Militant ladies singing "Rock of Ages." Bad time to walk out of saloon with two children. Unfavorable impressions. Somebody bound to recognize me. Boys anxious to leave. Couldn't stay there all night. Only one solution. Put on mask. Clown hat. Gave boys pails. Picked up pumpkin. Said let's step lively. Left bar moving fast. Sammy turned right. Roy left. I stopped. Mask fell off. Singing stopped. Ladies stared. More than I thought. Looked like Tabernacle Choir. Flashbulb went off. Man from local paper. Boys back. Said what are we waiting for? Couldn't say. More flashbulbs. Comments form ladies. Left in quiet, dignified manner. Suggested going home. Enough Halloween for one year.

Boys wanted more trick or treats. Said they'd meet me at the car. Asked if they were sure they could find it. Said they were sure. Let them go. Went around corner to where I'd left car. Not there. Possibly not right place. Tried next block. Cut over a block. Suddenly thought of kids. Find car gone. Frightened. Nowhere to turn. Panic. Went back to where I'd left them. Not there. Possibly not right place.

Tried next block. Other blocks. Checked all pirates and clowns. Not many out. Raining too hard. Kids going to be soaked. Maggie furious. No time for aimless running around. Time for decisive action. Take bull by horns. Call Maggie. Ask her what to do.

Went up to house. Rang bell. Asked man if I could use phone. Man said well he'd be son of a gun. Words to that effect. Woman called out. Asked who it was. Man called back. "Pagliacci," he said. I'd forgotten about clown hat. Man said phone was in hall. "I'll hold your pumpkin," he said. Forgotten that too.

Maggie answered. Chose words carefully so as not to alarm her. "Nothing to be alarmed about," I said. "Problems are solved best if we don't indulge in recriminations and personalities."

"What happened?" she asked. "The boys said you were supposed to meet them at the car—" I said, "You mean Sammy and Roy?" She said yes, those were the ones she meant. "When you didn't show up they phoned and I went in and picked them up. I couldn't imagine—" Told her it was slight misunderstanding. Asked her where she had picked them up. Precisely. Told her I'd be right home. Thanked man for use of phone. Man said don't mention it, tiger. Tiger? Glanced in hall mirror. Dye from wet clown hat had left orange streaks forehead to chin. Man handed me jack-o'-lantern. Woman said she hoped I liked popcorn balls. Said sure. Told me nice surprise for me when I opened pumpkin.

Found car O.K. Home. Put car in garage. Boys still up. Maggie looked at me. Closed her eyes. I said, "I'll tell you what happened." Maggie said, "I don't want to know—" I said, "O.K." Maggie said, "What happened?" Explained about clown hat. Inferior dye. She said clown hat didn't cause all the foam. Told her not foam—soapsuds.

"While the boys were waiting in the car they soaped the windshield," I said. "Had to drive home with my head out the window. What with the rain and the soap—"

Maggie said I must be proud of the boys. Chips off the old block. Voice sounded unnatural. Strained. Told her soaping the family windows didn't count. Supposed to play pranks on others. Sammy said they did. In the rest room. Threw toilet paper around. Wrote on mirror.

Told them not to tell stories. He hadn't learned to write yet. Said no but he had learned to print. Copied identity card on mirror. My name. My address. Phone number. Didn't lose my temper. Always try to be good sport. Hoped Emil felt the same.

Roy looking in jack-o'-lantern. Asked how come it was full of popcorn balls. Told him never mind. Maggie said where had kids gotten swizzle sticks? Asked her if she was going to put them to bed or let them stay up all night.

Sammy said how come my face looked so funny? Maggie said don't annoy the tiger. Took them upstairs. Poured myself a drink. Poured two. One might spill. Washed face. Got rid of suds anyhow.

Maggie came in. Asked how I was feeling. Told her great. "You were right about Halloween," she said. "I never really appreciated it before. The way the boys were talking made me realize there was something special about it—a sort of magic."

She had a point. How else was I going to explain my picture in the paper? Coming out of a saloon with two small boys. Wearing clown hat. Carrying pumpkin. Ladies in background singing hymns.

"Magic is the only word," I said.

Huckleberry Finn—Get Lost

I got to thinking the other day that boyhoods sure aren't what they used to be.

"You know," I said to Maggie, "your typical boyhood doesn't amount to a hill of beans these days. You ever think of that?"

She said yes, she thought about it a lot. All the time. I knew she was only saying it to make me feel good.

"Look at Daniel Boone," I said, "killed a bear when he was only about eight. Look at Huckleberry Finn. Look at Penrod."

"I'm looking," she said.

"Now look at me. The other morning at breakfast I was telling a story about when I was a boy. Sammy went over and began playing with the cat. Roy started reading the back of a cereal box."

"Oh well," she said, "the first thing in the morning—"

"When my father was telling a story about his boyhood we used to hang on every word. We couldn't get enough of his stories. And my grandfather. And now—"

119

"You shouldn't take everything so personally."

"Nobody's taking anything personally," I said. "Look at the people on the TV talk shows—the great childhoods they all had. Went into show business when they could barely walk, grew up in Hell's Kitchen with all the gangsters, had tea with the Prince of Wales—"

Maggie shrugged. "People in show business—"

"It's not because they're anything special—they just get the breaks is all. And it's not fair. Because inside every American boy is imprisoned a Huckleberry Finn trying to get free."

She studied me for a minute and shook her head. "Except you," she said. "I don't think you even had a Howard Cosell trying to get free."

I went over to the sink and got myself half a glass of water. "I wasn't thinking of myself—it's the kids. I'd like to give them some bright childhood memories while there's still time. Something they can look back on with pride. If they're ever on a talk show I don't want them to have to take a back seat to anybody."

I called the boys into the room. They looked at me and at each other. "We haven't done anything," Roy said.

I looked at Maggie. "You see?" I turned back to them. "Boys," I said, "what kind of childhood would you say you've had? So far?"

Roy said he thought about average.

Sammy said his childhood would be okay if he had a minibike and a lot more pizza.

"Okay," I said, "looking back, what stands out in your memory? What are some high spots?"

They took a moment to think and then they both started talking at once. A Valentine party, staying up late to watch *King Kong*, going to camp, the time I backed into the grape arbor, pulling taffy—I told them to stop. It was such a pathetic little parade of memories I couldn't stand it. I told them to go out and play.

"What can I do?" I asked Maggie. "How can I give them memories to take into their later years?"

"Take them to Altoona on a bus," she said. "That's something you don't forget."

"I was thinking of things like going down the Mississippi on a raft, having lunch with the Six Million Dollar Man."

"You could take them to see Wardell Dugan," Maggie said, "he lives over near Caledonia." I stared at her. "He won a Pulitzer Prize for something back in the fifties," she said, "there was a piece about him in last Sunday's paper."

I nodded. Some great conversation piece that would be in years to come. "My father once took me to see somebody named Wardell Dugan. I don't know why." That would make Merv and Dinah sit up and listen.

Maggie said, well, if I had a better idea. "Boys," I said, "how would you like to go and see Wardell Dugan?" They said fine.

He didn't look much like a Pulitzer Prize winner—a gray-haired fellow in overalls, living in an old farmhouse all by himself. I said I'd brought the boys out for a little visit if he had the time. All the time in the world he said. He seemed real pleased to see us.

I sat down at the kitchen table and Mr. Dugan got a half bottle of cherry soda out of the ice box. I explained that I was on a diet, but the boys each had a glass. He showed them some of the things he had around the kitchen. A box of arrowheads, a horseshoe carved out of wood, a few stuffed animals, an army hat. It was a great kitchen for boys.

I noticed that Mr. Dugan used expressions like "ain't" and "nohow" quite a lot. I didn't know what he'd gotten his prize for —something like folklore most likely. I asked him how he'd felt when he'd heard he'd won. He said not what you'd expect. "Natural I felt excited and puffed up, but kind of solemn too—like I wasn't sure if I was worthy or not."

Sammy said he knew what he meant. He had won a prize once bobbing for apples and that was the way he felt. Roy said he'd won a prize once in a sack race and that was exactly the way he felt. Mr. Dugan said, well then, he didn't have to explain.

"Don't look at me," I told him, "I never won a prize. For anything."

"You're young yet," he said. He was holding one of the arrowheads, polishing it with his thumb. "The only thing I feel a little sorry about is not having any family left. Most times I get

121

along fine by myself, but then when something like this happens you'd like to have somebody to share it with. That's why I was so pleased to have you folks come out here. You read about me in the paper, did you?" I said I hadn't seen the article, but my wife had. "I've got it right here if you'd like to see it," he said.

The item Maggie had seen was at the top of the page. "Interviewed at his retirement home, former Pulitzer Prize winner Albert Gordon told your reporter—" Albert Gordon? Next to it was a story about a local man who had entered a prize pumpkin in the county fair. That one was Wardell Dugan. Maggie had transposed the names, that was all.

"It's out in the barn if you'd like to see it," Mr. Dugan said. I told him sure.

When we were ready to leave he came over to the car. "Can't tell you how much I appreciate this," he said. I told him it was our pleasure.

He pushed his hat to the back of his head and looked out over the fields. "Never figured to amount to much of anything," he said. "Just started to grow the big pumpkins as a kind of pastime. Then there was the prize and the story in the paper—the boys coming here for my autograph and you taking my picture and well —it seems like it's made it all worthwhile."

I told him we'd be back soon and we headed home. The boys couldn't wait to get in the house and tell their mother.

"We had pizza," Roy said, "and saw the giant pumpkin and Dad went down the barn steps backward."

"The man gave us each a real arrowhead," Sammy said, "and we had frozen custard and Dad took us through a car wash that even cleaned his glasses."

Maggie sent them upstairs to wash. Then she sat down and looked at me expectantly. I explained about the mixup in the two stories. "The old fellow was so pleased to see us I couldn't let him find out. I even promised to bring the boys back again. I thought maybe I could take him some cupcakes or something."

"I'll bake him a pie," Maggie said, "and I'm coming too. I'm not going to let you have all the good memories." She frowned. "You're limping—did you hurt your foot?"

"It's nothing," I said. "I was taking their picture in the barn and I stepped back to focus. I didn't notice the hay chute."

She came over to me. "Your shirt—it's soaked."

"Yes. Well, the afternoon had been sort of a washout, I thought, so I got the boys pizza and frozen custard. There was this car wash next door and they said they'd never been through one. Well, I drove in and nothing happened. I decided I must be off the track so I rolled down the window to look. That's when it started. You know that detergent really smarts."

"Well, you did it," she said, "you really did. I knew that somehow you'd give them a day to remember, but nothing like this."

"Oh, shucks," I said, "it's nothing." Still, as Maggie says, it did work out pretty well even if it wasn't exactly the way I'd planned. But then, maybe it's a mistake to try to plan memories. Better to just go along and let them happen. And if it's true that each individual has a Huckleberry Finn inside, let him stay there.

Imperfect Listener

Who would expect you could get into a jam just by trying to be a good listener? It happened to me. I had read this article at the dentist's office. It said a good listener was rare indeed and consequently was popular and in demand and so on. I decided to give it a try.

As I walked up the block toward the house that evening I spotted Gretchen playing jacks in her friend Norma's front yard. "Well," I said, "what have you two been up to all day?"

Gretchen shrugged. "Nothing special."

"Playing hopscotch, I'll bet," I went on. There were chalked squares all over the sidewalk. The girls didn't answer.

Norma's mother, Mrs. Mizner, came out on the porch. "Was there something you wanted?" she asked me. She is a large, belligerent woman and busybody of international renown.

"No," I said, "I was just passing the time with the girls." Mrs. Mizner and I had never exactly seen eye to eye. It occurred to me that if I could draw her out and make her realize I was a good listener it would be a real accomplishment.

"Well," I went on, "it's easy to see how you've been spending the afternoon." I was referring to the lines of washing I could see strung out in the backyard. Unfortunately before I had finished the remark a man stepped out on the porch with a can of beer in his hand. It was not Mr. Mizner.

She looked at him and then at me. Her face got red. "For your information this gentleman happens to be my cousin from Duluth."

"Well," I said, "a lot of nice country around there."

The man turned and went back into the house. Mrs. Mizner gave me a final glare and went inside and slammed the door. To tell the truth, I don't think I could ever be a good listener as far as she was concerned.

When I arrived home I found Maggie in the kitchen. "Hello," I said, "what kind of a day did you have?"

"Ecstatic," she said. She had her sewing table upside down on the kitchen floor and was drilling holes in the legs to put casters in.

"Here," I said, "I told you I'd do that."

"Yes I know. Did you remember to call the man about the insurance?"

"I'll do it tomorrow first thing." I took the drill from her hand and put it on the shelf. "Now, come on, I'll fix a drink and you can tell me all about it."

"What is all this?" she asked when we were settled in the living room. "What are you trying to find out?"

"Everything," I told her, "what you did, what you thought about."

Maggie said, "The garbage man."

I waited for her to go on, smiling and nodding as I sipped my drink. "Yes, the garbage man came, I see. What else happened?"

"He didn't come," she said. "There's a loose button on your jacket—leave it on the chair."

"Maggie, you don't seem to understand." I got up and took off my coat. "I'm making every effort to establish some line of communication between us."

She set her glass on the coffee table. "Did you put any vermouth at all in these?"

I picked up the pitcher and refilled my glass. I wished the fellow who had written the article had been present. He might have learned a few things about good listening. "What's happened to us?" I asked. "It seems day by day we're drifting farther apart."

"Well," she said, "it's been windy lately."

"I ask you a simple question about how you spend your time and you change the subject."

"I'm sorry," she said. "I had lunch with Yul Brynner. Afterward we flew up to Green Bay to watch the Packers work out."

"I'm trying to be serious."

"I don't believe it. A big house and yard for me to look after not to mention four children, and you sit in your air-conditioned office and wonder how I manage to pass the time."

"I was only trying to have a little friendly conversation."

"Well, stop trying," she said, "you're not cut out for it." She got to her feet. "Now, if you'll excuse me, I'll see about dinner." She started out of the room.

"Say," I said heartily, "something sure smells good. What are we having tonight?"

"Elk," Maggie said. She went out and closed the door.

In a few minutes the phone in the hall rang. It was Maggie's mother. Here was a fresh opportunity. She could make a good listener out of Leo Durocher.

"How are you?" I asked her. "What have you been up to lately?"

She said, "What do you mean by that?"

"I'm talking about your sewing circle and the women's auxiliary. What do you hear from the Gray Ladies?"

"You sound funny, dear," she said. "Have you been to an office party?"

"I don't seem to be getting through to you," I said. "When we don't hear anything from you for a while, we wonder. Are you taking proper care of yourself? How are your roses this year?"

"Dear, this is long distance," she said. "Could I speak to my daughter Maggie? Your wife," she added so there could be no chance of a mistake. I waited to see if she was going to say the mother of her grandchildren, but she didn't.

I called Maggie and went back to the living room. Through the door I could hear part of the conversation.

"Why no," Maggie said, "everything's fine. Why should he be trying to cover up something?" There was a considerable pause.

"No," Maggie said, "just a couple of martinis. Maybe you had a bad connection." Another pause. "Well, how would I know what he had on the way home?" I went over and closed the door. Any conversation between a mother and daughter should be considered sacred.

After a little while Sammy came in. He was wearing a sombrero with tassels hanging all around. I hadn't seen it before. "Well," I said, "I see you've gotten yourself a new hat."

He looked at me through the fringe. "It's not new," he said.

"It's new to me," I said, "and after all that's what counts." He continued to look at me. "Isn't it?" I said.

Sammy said he didn't know.

"Come on over and talk to me," I said. Then I added, "Son." He approached my chair by walking around three sides of the room. "It's been a long time since we've had a man-to-man talk," I remarked. "What did you do today?"

"Nothing," he said.

"You certainly must have done something," I said.

"I didn't tip over the table in the kitchen," he said, "Gretchen did it."

"Gretchen did nothing of the kind," I told him. "Your mother did it."

"She did?"

"Yes she did, so don't go giving me any stories."

"Boy, she sure must be mad."

"That has nothing to do with it," I said. "She wasn't angry when she turned over the table."

"Gee," Sammy said, "wait till I tell the other kids."

"Forget it," I told him. "You're not going around the neighborhood telling wild tales about your mother. You're going to stand right there and tell me what you've been doing all day—every single thing."

He spread his hands helplessly. "But I didn't do anything." His lip was beginning to tremble.

Maggie came in from the kitchen. "Haven't you anything better to do than bully your child?" She knelt down and put her arm around him, tipping the sombrero down over his face.

"Dammit all," I said, "what is this—some conspiracy of silence? I can't even talk to my own family."

"It sounds as though you were trying to talk to the whole block," Maggie said in a voice unnecessarily modulated.

I gave up. Being a good listener just wasn't in the cards. Not with my family. And the fellow who wrote the article could go soak his head. Dinner, which usually sounds like the Army-Navy game, was deathly silent. Afterward I went out for a walk.

I got back around nine-thirty. Maggie glanced up from her chair as I came in. Then she took another look and jumped up.

"What happened?" she asked. "There's a big scratch on your cheek and your lip's all puffed up."

The kids came running in. Gretchen grabbed my hand. "Daddy, will you have to go to the hospital?"

"Oh, for God sakes," I said, "you'd think nobody around here had ever seen a fat lip before."

Sammy said, "I bet the others are all dead. I bet Daddy knocked everybody out in the whole saloon."

I patted him on the head. "You're a nice boy," I said. "Now get lost."

I lay down on the couch and Maggie got a cloth and started dabbing at my face. "You want to tell me about it?"

"Not especially."

"Aw come on." She put the cloth on my eye.

"Well," I said, "ever since I came home from the office I have been trying to be a good listener."

"A good listener—" she said.

"Yes. There was this article I read. It said everybody likes to talk, but a good listener is greatly in demand."

"And you were practicing—"

"Trying to," I said. "But I decided to give it up. Then after I'd left the house I thought about it a little more. Somehow I hated to give up so easily—to admit defeat."

"Naturally."

"I happened to be passing the tavern, so I thought I'd go in and try it on Otto."

She nodded. "Sammy was on the right track."

"You know how it is with bartenders—always listening to other people's troubles. It seemed to me maybe Otto would welcome the chance to confide in a sympathetic listener. Take it easy on that eye."

"I'm sorry." She lighted a cigarette and handed it to me. "And then?"

"Thanks. Well, then I remarked that he seemed to be doing a pretty good business and he said not bad. I said I bet he must be making four hundred a week. He wanted to know whose business that was. Well, the way I had it figured if somebody has a good thing going he likes to talk about it."

"But not Otto?"

"Not at the moment. It seems the Internal Revenue people are going over his returns. Somebody gave them a tip that Otto had been holding out on them."

"Surely he doesn't suspect you?"

"He suspects everybody, but right now I'm at the top of the list. Anyhow I decided to change the subject. I mentioned that I hadn't seen Cora around lately."

Maggie said, "Oh dear."

"Oh dear what?" I said. "Apparently there's something I ought to know."

"Cora went back to her mother's a week ago. It's all over town. I'm sure I told you."

"I see. That must have been before I decided to be a good listener. Well, you never saw anybody carry on the way he did. Said

129

if there was one thing he couldn't stand it was a wiseacre." I glanced up at Maggie. "You know, it's been a long time since I've heard that term—'wiseacre.'"

"Go on."

"I'm afraid Otto is not a well-adjusted person. The more he talked the more excited he got. I think it's a mistake for a person with psychological problems to tend bar."

"No question about it," Maggie said.

"Finally he pointed his finger at me and told me to get out and stay out. I told him I'd never been thrown out of a bar before and I didn't intend to start with a crummy joint like his."

"I guess you were mistaken."

"Yes—Otto really moves fast for a big man. You wouldn't believe it."

"The—ah—police weren't involved?"

"No, nothing like that. It was all handled in a civilized manner."

"Then I wouldn't worry," Maggie said. "Otto will cool down before long."

"Otto can freeze solid for all I care."

Maggie put down the cloth and started to chuckle. "I'm sorry, but it is funny."

"It's always nice to be able to see the bright side."

"It's the way you tell it," she said, "you know you have a wonderful knack for stories."

"You really think so?"

"Certainly. It wouldn't surprise me if this turned out to be one of your favorites."

I sat up touching my lip gingerly. "I suppose it does have some humorous aspects."

"Why don't you go to bed," she suggested, "and I'll fix you a hot toddy." It sounded like a good idea.

It must have been two or three in the morning when I woke up. I tapped Maggie's shoulder to see if she was awake. "Huh?" she said. "What is it?"

"It's you," I told her, "it's been you all along."

"Oh?" she said. "What has?"

"You have," I said. "You're the perfect listener. I just realized it."

Maggie raised herself on one elbow and stared down at me in the darkness. After a minute she lay back down with a sigh. "Tell me more," she said.

Farewell, St. Nick

I've given it a lot of thought and it seems to me there is no good way to tell your child the truth about Santa Claus. You can say that he's a symbol of good will and the joy of giving and so on. But a kid doesn't give a hoot about symbols. All he knows is that there's this jolly fat guy who has given him all this nice stuff and has always been his friend. Even when Mommy and Daddy have been mean and unfair, Santa has been true—he has been on his side. And now you stand there and tell him it is all a hoax and a fraud. It is the end of the age of innocence and the natural tendency is to put it off—to string it out as long as possible. Although there are those who think you should tell the child as early as possible. Get it over with.

I'm thinking now of Ross and Shelley Forepaugh, who told their boy Bradley the truth about Santa when he was barely four. While they were at it they told him about the Easter Bunny, the Tooth Fairy and the Stork. It was too much. Up to that time he had never considered that babies came from anywhere—they were just there like doors and radiators. Of course the first thing he did was break the news to all the other little kids on the block.

"I wouldn't mind so much if he could keep it straight," I remarked to Maggie, "but he's got it all scrambled. Not that I'm surprised. When I first learned about sex it took me quite a while to get it straightened out and I didn't have the Easter Bunny and the Tooth Fairy to mix me up."

"It's a break really," Maggie said, "because none of the kids believed what he told them. If he'd had his facts straight, he might have been more convincing."

It didn't matter so much actually, because Ross and Shelley broke up shortly after that and moved away. That's another thing —I feel that you shouldn't tell a kid about Santa unless you're pretty sure you're going to stay married for a while. Don't pull all the rugs out from under him at once. What with the home, the school, and the government as shaky as they are these days, a kid needs something to cling to—Tooth Fairy or something. But of course the time comes eventually when you have to tell them. Sammy was nearly seven and it was time.

"I'm really dreading this," I told Maggie, "a child's faith is a very fragile, very touching thing. You realize we've had Santa here every year since Kit was a baby—fifteen years. And now it's over— the end of an era."

"Have a cup of coffee," she said.

"I can't even remember how we told the others."

"You know Kit," Maggie said, "she's always had to run things, even when she was tiny. Christmas just wasn't big enough for Kit and Santa too. She must have phased him out between age five and six.

"And Roy—well, he never was much concerned with Santa Claus. All he cared about was getting his presents up to his room so he could start taking them apart."

"Sammy's different," I said, "you know that." He always had been different. He was the sort of skinny, big-eyed kid you used to see on magazine covers with the shabby coat and the long red muffler wrapped around his neck, his nose pressed against the window of the toy store.

"I can tell him if you'd rather not," Maggie said.

"I'll tell him," I said, "no need to make a federal case of it."

Sammy was in his room drawing a picture. I asked him how everything was going. He didn't know about everything he said.

"You know, Sammy, things aren't always what they seem."

"Well," he said, "the birds and bees sure aren't."

Bradley apparently had gotten in his two cents' worth.

"I'm thinking of Santa Claus," I said, "did I ever tell you about Christmas when I was a boy?"

"Yup," he said.

I suppose we tend to repeat ourselves, talking about the things we like and Christmas has always been one of the things I like best. What I like about it is everything. What can match the smell of a room of fresh-cut greens—balsam, fir, and spruce with an overlay of baking cookies? Does anything taste better than turkey gravy on mashed potatoes? No it doesn't.

Music—no other occasion has given us more than one decent song. Christmas has at least a dozen that are first rate.

And of course the Christmas tree, which I consider one of the great inventions of all time, standing right up there with the soul kiss and the chocolate soda.

Maybe, I thought, the tree would be a good place to start with Sammy. I asked him if he knew where Christmas trees came from. Turned out he did.

"They come from a seed," he said. "Everything comes from a seed. People even."

I said what I meant was how did the tree get set up in our living room with all the colored lights and gold balls and angels and candy canes.

"You left out tinsel," he said.

"I didn't leave it out," I said, "I hadn't gotten to it. You always put the tinsel on last."

"Some people call it rain," he said. "I like tinsel better. It looks more like tinsel." He frowned at his picture. "Why do some people say rain?"

"Some people will say anything," I said. "What are you drawing a picture of?"

He said it was a midget eating graham crackers.

"It's no good," I said to Maggie. "I can't tell him."

"No rush," she said.

"I was talking to Hux about my problem," I said. "He laughed."

"Hux never laughs."

"Yeah he did. Asked if I realized the problems facing mankind. Pollution, energy crunch, endangered species—"

"I've heard it before."

"Twenty-seven items," I said. "And at the very end he added telling Sammy about Santa Claus. That's when he laughed."

"Probably thought he was being clever."

"They have an aluminum tree," I said, "with blue lights. Who cares what a barbarian like that thinks?"

People sometimes call me materialistic because I love all the stuff of Christmas. Maggie's sister once told me I didn't understand the Christmas spirit meaning things like peace on earth, joy, good will. Hogwash, I said.

"Listen, if we devote one day out of the year to colored lights and candy canes, that's nothing to be ashamed of. But if we devote one day a year to peace and joy and good will—why then I think we've got a problem." She didn't have an answer for that. As a matter of fact, she wasn't even listening. Be that as it may.

I can't imagine Christmas in a warm climate. There's something about snow—the way it halos the streetlights and crunches on the walk, the way it smells. Maggie said snow didn't have a smell.

"Are you kidding?" I asked. "It's like the sea. Each year when you go to the shore for the first time you smell the ocean and it's just the way you remembered it. Exactly. An hour later it's gone. Same with snow. The first cold morning after a snowfall you step out on the porch and take a deep breath and it smells just like it did when you were five."

"I can go along with Christmas," Maggie said, "and I can go

135

along with nostalgia, but when you put them together, it's too much."

The next time I talked with Sammy he was playing with his Indian village. "Sammy," I said, "did you ever stop to think how hard it would be for one person to go around the whole world in one night with a team of reindeer?"

"You're talking about Santa Claus," he said.

"Right," I said. "Or imagine him coming down the chimney with that sack of toys—a bike maybe or a pair of skis."

"Bobby Latham's father plays Santa at their house," he said, "dresses up in a red suit and passes out presents. Only he doesn't fool anybody on account of he has a real high voice and glasses."

"I don't think he's trying to fool anybody," I said, "it's just make believe—like your Indian village. You don't believe they're real Indians do you?"

He looked up at me. "They're two inches high and they're made out of plastic."

"Well," I said, "there you are." I went downstairs.

"Did you tell him?" Maggie asked.

"God knows," I said.

I looked out the window. "Can you imagine someone like Rodney Latham dressing up in a red suit and whiskers and trying to make his kids think he's Santa?"

"What's this I've heard so often about having tolerance for other people's ideas?"

"Other people's good ideas, sure," I said. "But tolerance has its limits and a stupid idea like that is one of them."

I asked the other kids to see if they could get me a reading on Sammy's present Christmas feelings. They reported back that he seemed to have a pretty realistic posture Santa Clauswise. Fair enough, I thought.

On Christmas Eve we let Sammy stay up to help decorate the tree. He seemed to get a big kick out of it. I hoped it would make up for what had been lost. That look of early-morning rapture— the colored lights reflected in the all-believing eyes. I remembered it so well.

"You know," I said, "it was just fifteen years ago that Santa first came to our house and every year he's been coming back with his surprises and good cheer. Until now. This Christmas he won't be coming. But that doesn't mean he won't be back. Some day you'll be having children of your own—"

"I know how that works," Sammy said.

"I'm sure you do," I told him.

I guess it was about as nice a Christmas as we've had. During the midmorning lull, Maggie put through a call to her mother. Sammy said he was going out to play with Bradley. "Bradley?" I said.

"Yeah," he said, "he and his mom came back to spend Christmas with his mom's folks. His granddad took him down to see Santa. And you know what?" Sammy's face had a look of wonder. "He believes—he really does."

"Well, great," I said, "you wouldn't say anything, would you?"

"Heck no," he said, "it's sort of fun—you know?"

"I know," I told him. I watched the two of them building a snowman across the street. Sammy had on his new mittens and ski hat.

"Maggie," I said, "it's cold out there, how come Sammy isn't wearing that long red muffler of his?"

"He doesn't have a long red muffler," she said, "he's never had one—oh, hello, Mother—"

Funny, I could have sworn—still, Sammy didn't seem to be bothered by anything. Apparently Maggie thought so too. I could overhear her voice from the hall.

"Uh huh, the first time in fifteen years. Yes," she went on, "I was a little concerned, but all in all I thought he came through it very well."

Courtin' Time

As I remarked to my wife, psychologists tell us that a child's first date can determine the outcome of his future courtship and marriage.

"Bunk," Maggie said. "What psychologist said that?"

"All of them," I said.

"Yeah?" she said. "What about *your* first date?"

I tried to remember. All I could recall was the girl's name—Sheila Huntzinger. Either that or Rosie Glick. "That's beside the point," I told her. "Roy is a shy, sensitive kid. His first date—"

"It's a little, informal dance," she said. "He's taking Karen Wesley—they've grown up together."

"Not yet they haven't," I said.

"Have you seen her lately?" she asked. "She's a delightful child."

I'd seen her. Slender as a gazelle, silky hair, delicate features—

the real take-charge type. Poor Roy. "There's still a week," I said, "with the right coaching—"

"He already knows how to dance," Maggie said, "and he has nice manners. What else does he need?"

"Just about everything." I called Roy and he came in with Sammy trailing behind. "Roy," I said, "I understand you're taking Karen to the dance next week." He said he guessed so.

"You're going to be dating a girl," I told him, "and that's no place for guesswork. You've got to have your facts straight. Now, I don't know how much you know about girls—"

He said he could explain it better using chickens. "You see the hen lays the egg—"

"Never mind the chickens," I told him. "That's not what I'm talking about."

"Works the same way with ducks," Sammy said. "Only difference is they can swim."

"Forget the chickens *and* the ducks," I said. "I'm talking about going up on Karen's porch, ringing the bell, bringing her out to the car. It's not the same as picking up Sparky for baseball practice."

For one thing, Sammy said, he wouldn't be wearing sneakers. Roy said he wouldn't be taking his mitt either. Sammy said maybe he should take his mitt. "You never know, you might get a chance to play a little catch between dances."

I turned to Maggie. "You see?"

"If only you wouldn't make such a production out of it," she said.

"Life is a production," I told her, "it's time you found that out."

Roy's trouble was he treated the whole thing as a joke. "I've tried to help him," I told Maggie, "he doesn't realize that a bad date can be a traumatic experience."

She said how true. "And not just the bad ones either."

"The Lord knows I've done my share, taught him card tricks, funny stories, how to make an egg disappear from a hat—"

Maggie said she thought I'd done more than my share.

I decided the thing to do was have a practice date. Sammy agreed to play Karen and I would play her father. I wanted Maggie to play the mother, but at the last minute I couldn't find her. Typically enough. I had expected trouble from Sammy but he entered into it with fine spirit, putting on an old wig of Maggie's, makeup, and perfume. He tripped on his high heels and fell halfway down the stairs, but otherwise he did fine.

Roy went out and knocked on the front door. "Come in," I said, "well, nice to see you Roy, how are your folks?"

He said okay except that his mom was mad at his dad. I said, "Oh?" "Yes," he said, "she thinks this practice idea is a lot of baloney and she wouldn't have any part of it. She went out to water the garden." I said, "Oh." "Where's your wife?" he asked.

Watering the garden, I started to say before I realized I was supposed to be Karen's dad. "I don't know," I said, "she ought to be around somewhere."

"Is she mad too?"

"I don't believe anybody's mad, Roy, I think you're just imagining it."

He nodded. "She said of all the hare-brained schemes my dad ever had—"

I told Roy he shouldn't tell tales out of school. He said I shouldn't have asked. I said I knew.

Sammy said hello to Roy. Roy said hello to Sammy. "That's a pretty dress you have on, Karen."

Sammy looked down at his T shirt with the paint and chili on it. "I got it just for you," he said. "And I put on two kinds of perfume. My Sin on one side and My Joy on the other."

"I know," Roy said, "I could smell you all the way out to the road."

"Cut," I said. "You don't talk about smelling anything on a date. Talk about books or the weather or TV."

Roy asked Sammy if he'd read any good books. Sammy said no. Roy said it had been hot lately.

"Sure has," Sammy said, "I been sweating like a goat."

I didn't say anything. Roy asked if he'd seen any good TV programs. Sammy started telling the plot of an episode of Gilligan's

Island. After a couple of minutes I interrupted. "Do you see what the problem is here? These shows are reruns and every kid in the neighborhood has seen them three or four times. Roy, it's up to you to change the subject."

"Okay," he said, "have you read any good books lately?" I said he's already asked that. "This time I'm asking you," he said.

I couldn't think of any book I'd read good or bad. "*Gone With the Wind*," I said finally.

I heard a cough. Maggie was standing by the door. "Gone With the What?" she said.

"Ah, there you are, my dear," I said. "Here's young Roy come to take Karen to the dance." She didn't say anything, just rolled her eyes up to the heavens. Well, maybe it did sound a little stiff, but what did she expect, letting me carry the ball all by myself? "We've been having a most interesting chat."

Sammy was staring at me with his mouth open. The lipstick pointed up his missing front teeth and the mascara gave the appearance of two black eyes almost hidden by the sagging wig. Roy gave a little bow toward Maggie. "It's easy to see where your daughter gets her looks," he said.

"Thanks," Maggie said, "you're a sweet child."

"The trouble is he's so sure of himself," I said to Maggie.

"That's bad?" she said.

"It's just that I had to learn everything the hard way," I said. "I guess I was looking forward to teaching it all to him, helping him. But he doesn't want any help."

I helped him anyway. Like staying up with him to watch Fred Astaire on the late movie. Only when Maggie came down at twelve-thirty I was asleep on the couch and Roy was watching Johnny Carson. He thought it would be more help than the other. "Take away the tap dancing," he said, "and what have you got?"

As I said to Maggie, "I guess it's pretty dumb to try to copy a movie star."

"I don't know," she said, "you used to copy George Raft when we were first dating. That hair oil was murder on blouses."

I smiled. "Those were the days."

"You used to go around with your eyes half closed, flipping a half dollar," she said in a kind of faraway voice. "One night you flipped it out the car window and we never could find it. And it was your gas money, remember? We had to leave your dad's car on Lincoln Boulevard and walk home."

"I always thought Raft was highly overrated," I said.

Since I was playing chauffeur, I had the car washed and vacuumed. When I got home I found Roy was washed, brushed, combed, and polished. I started to mix an old fashioned. "Thought of a couple of limericks you might use," I said, "sort of ice-breakers."

He said he didn't need ice-breakers. "You're not going to have a drink first, are you?" I said of course not. I was mixing it for your mom. "Don't get any on you," he said. After a moment he asked if I didn't have a plainer tie. I could remember my early dates—entire evenings of sustained panic. Roy seemed more like a vice-president of something—as if he'd skipped the awkward years completely. In a funny way it seemed too bad.

Driving along I glanced over at him. Somehow he had managed to get a streak of mud on his shoe. His tie had worked over to one side and he was beginning to sweat. Nice-looking kid.

I slowed down as we approached the house. "Don't stop," he said in a hoarse voice, "keep going." I drove on by. His face was a damp gray. I asked if there was anything wrong. Something in his throat he said. His face was frozen into a mask.

"You know," I said casually, "my first date with Mom I pushed her into a fish pond. Accidentally. A little later I was showing a magic trick and turned over the punch bowl." And on and on until by the time we'd gone around the block he'd recovered from his stage fright. Of course the date I described never really happened. What I'd done was take incidents from half a dozen dates and weave them together. So, what of it? Roy would never know.

As I watched him going up the walk, tripping over an uneven spot, I thought of the road he was about to take—the male-female encounters in their unending variety that lay ahead. It was a long road and rocky, filled with flowers and thorns, high adventure and low comedy, frustration and intrigue, triumph and humiliation, delight and despair. And I knew there wasn't anything better I could have wished for him. Stick with it Roy, I wanted to call after him—way to go in there.